# GCSE
# Combined Science
# Biology

There's a lot of Biology to learn in GCSE Combined Science... but this fantastic CGP book explains the facts, theory and practical skills with the clearest study notes around!

On top of all that, there are exam-style questions for every topic — plus a set of Biology practice exam papers to *really* test you on what you've learned.

We've also included fully-worked answers, so it's easy to mark your work and learn from any mistakes. Everything you need for a top grade!

## How to access your free Online Edition

This book includes a free Online Edition to read on your PC, Mac or tablet.
You'll just need to go to **cgpbooks.co.uk/extras** and enter this code:

2910 2469 0006 9104

By the way, this code only works for one person. If somebody else has used this book before you, they might have already claimed the Online Edition.

# Complete
# Revision & Practice
Everything you need to pass the exams!

# Contents

Throughout this book you'll see grade stamps like these:

These grade stamps help to show how difficult the questions are.
Remember — to get a top grade you need to be able to answer **all** the questions, not just the hardest ones.

In the real exams, some questions test how well you can structure an answer (as well as your scientific knowledge). In this book, we've marked these questions with an asterisk (*).

## Practical Skills

## Practice Exams

Published by CGP

Editors: Luke Bennett, Ellen Burton, Mary Falkner, Daniel Fielding and Emily Forsberg.

Contributors: Paddy Gannon

From original material by Richard Parsons.

With thanks to Chris Lindle and Hayley Thompson for the proofreading.

With thanks to Jan Greenway for the copyright research.

Percentile growth chart on page 40 copyright © 2009 Royal College of Paediatrics and Child Health.

Definition of health on page 74 from: Preamble to the Constitution of the World Health Organization as adopted by the International Health Conference, New York, 19 June - 22 July 1946; signed on 22 July 1946 by the representatives of 61 States (Official Records of the World Health Organization, no. 2, p. 100) and entered into force on 7 April 1948.

With thanks to EYE OF SCIENCE/SCIENCE PHOTO LIBRARY for permission to reproduce the image of blood cells on page 168.

With thanks to SCIENCE PHOTO LIBRARY for permission to reproduce the image of a contraceptive implant on page 175.

With thanks to iStock.com/AbelBrata for permission to reproduce the image of a condom on page 175.

Every effort has been made to locate copyright holders and obtain permission to reproduce sources. For those sources where it has been difficult to trace the originator of the work, we would be grateful for information. If any copyright holder would like us to make an amendment to the acknowledgements, please notify us and we will gladly update the book at the next reprint. Thank you.

ISBN: 978 1 78294 877 3

Printed by Elanders Ltd, Newcastle upon Tyne.

Clipart from Corel®

# What to Expect in the Exams

Before you get cracking with your <u>revision</u> and <u>exam practice</u>, here's a <u>handy guide</u> to what you'll have to face in the exams — and the <u>special features</u> of this book that we've included especially to <u>help you</u>. You're welcome.

## 1. Sections are Covered in Different Papers

For GCSE Combined Science, you'll sit <u>six exam papers</u> at the <u>end</u> of your course, including <u>two biology exams</u>.

| Paper | Time | No. of marks | Sections Assessed |
|---|---|---|---|
| Biology 1 | 1 hr 10 mins | 60 | 1, 2, 3, 4 and 5 |
| Biology 2 | 1 hr 10 mins | 60 | 1, 6, 7, 8 and 9 |

## 2. There are Different Question Types

In each exam, you'll be expected to answer a mixture of <u>multiple-choice</u> questions, <u>calculations</u>, <u>short answer</u> questions, and one <u>longer, open response</u> question.

*We've marked open response questions in this book with an asterisk (\*).*

For <u>open response</u> questions, you'll be marked on the <u>structure</u> of your answer, not just its <u>scientific content</u>. So...

Fortunately, we've included loads of <u>questions</u> in this book, as well as a <u>set of practice papers</u> to give you the <u>best possible preparation</u> for the exams.

<u>Always</u> make sure:

- Your answer is <u>clear</u> and has a <u>logical structure</u>.
- The points you make <u>link together</u> and form a sensible <u>line of reasoning</u> (if appropriate for the question).
- You include <u>detailed, relevant information</u>.

## 3. You'll be Tested on Your Maths...

At least <u>20% of the total marks</u> for GCSE Combined Science will come from questions that test your <u>maths skills</u>. For these questions, always remember to:

*Look out for these <u>worked examples</u> in this book — they show you maths skills you'll need in the exam.*

- Show your <u>working</u> — you could get marks for this, even if your final answer's wrong.
- Check that you're using the right <u>units</u>.
- Make sure your answer is given to an appropriate number of <u>significant figures</u>.

## 4. ...and on Your Practical Skills

*Whenever one of the <u>core practicals</u> crops up in this book, it's marked up with stamps like these...*

*...and there's a whole section on Practical Skills on pages 144-148.*

- GCSE Combined Science contains <u>18 mandatory core practicals</u> that you'll do during the course. The <u>6 biology practicals</u> are covered in this book. You can be asked about these, and the practical skills involved in them, in the exams.
- At least <u>15% of the total marks</u> will be for questions that test your understanding of the practical activities and practical skills.
- For example, you might be asked to comment on the <u>design</u> of an experiment (the <u>apparatus</u> and <u>method</u>), make <u>predictions</u>, <u>analyse</u> or <u>interpret results</u>... Pretty much anything to do with planning and carrying out the investigations.

## 5. You'll Need to Know About Working Scientifically

<u>Working Scientifically</u> is all about how science is applied in the outside world by <u>real scientists</u>.

For example, you might be asked about ways that scientists <u>communicate</u> an idea to get their point across without being <u>biased</u>, or about the <u>limitations</u> of a scientific theory.

*Working Scientifically is covered on pages 2-16.*

You need to think about the <u>situation</u> that you've been given and use all your <u>scientific savvy</u> to answer the question. Always <u>read the question</u> and any <u>data</u> you've been given really carefully <u>before</u> you start writing your answer.

# The Scientific Method

This section isn't about how to 'do' science — but it does show you the way most scientists work.

## Scientists Come Up With **Hypotheses** — Then **Test** Them

1) Scientists try to explain things. They start by observing something they don't understand.

2) They then come up with a hypothesis — a possible explanation for what they've observed.

3) The next step is to test whether the hypothesis might be right or not. This involves making a prediction based on the hypothesis and testing it by gathering evidence (i.e. data) from investigations. If evidence from experiments backs up a prediction, you're a step closer to figuring out if the hypothesis is true.

Hundreds of years ago, we thought demons caused illness.

## **Several Scientists** Will **Test** a Hypothesis

1) Normally, scientists share their findings in peer-reviewed journals, or at conferences.

2) Peer-review is where other scientists check results and scientific explanations to make sure they're 'scientific' (e.g. that experiments have been done in a sensible way) before they're published. It helps to detect false claims, but it doesn't mean that findings are correct — just that they're not wrong in any obvious way.

3) Once other scientists have found out about a hypothesis, they'll start basing their own predictions on it and carry out their own experiments. They'll also try to reproduce the original experiments to check the results — and if all the experiments in the world back up the hypothesis, then scientists start to think the hypothesis is true.

4) However, if a scientist does an experiment that doesn't fit with the hypothesis (and other scientists can reproduce the results) then the hypothesis may need to be modified or scrapped altogether.

Then we thought it was caused by 'bad blood' (and treated it with leeches).

## If **All** the **Evidence** Supports a Hypothesis, It's **Accepted** — For Now

1) Accepted hypotheses are often referred to as theories. Our currently accepted theories are the ones that have survived this 'trial by evidence' — they've been tested many times over the years and survived.

2) However, theories never become totally indisputable fact. If new evidence comes along that can't be explained using the existing theory, then the hypothesising and testing is likely to start all over again.

Now we've collected more evidence, we know that illnesses that can be spread between people are due to microorganisms.

---

## Scientific models are constantly being refined...

The scientific method has been developed over time. Aristotle (a Greek philosopher) was the first person to realise that theories need to be based on observations. Muslim scholars then introduced the ideas of creating a hypothesis, testing it, and repeating work to check results.

# Models and Communication

Once scientists have made a <u>new discovery</u>, they <u>don't</u> just keep it to themselves. Oh no. Time to learn about how scientific discoveries are <u>communicated</u>, and the <u>models</u> that are used to represent theories.

## Theories Can Involve **Different Types** of **Models**

1) A <u>representational model</u> is a <u>simplified description</u> or <u>picture</u> of what's going on in real life. Like all models, it can be used to <u>explain observations</u> and <u>make predictions</u>. E.g. the <u>lock and key model</u> of enzyme action is a simplified way of showing how <u>enzymes</u> work (see p.26). It can be used to explain why enzymes only catalyse particular reactions.

*Scientists test models by carrying out experiments to check that the predictions made by the model happen as expected.*

2) <u>Computational models</u> use computers to make <u>simulations</u> of complex real-life processes, such as climate change. They're used when there are a <u>lot</u> of different <u>variables</u> (factors that change) to consider, and because you can easily <u>change their design</u> to take into account <u>new data</u>.

3) All models have <u>limitations</u> on what they can <u>explain</u> or <u>predict</u>. <u>Climate change models</u> have several limitations — for example, it's hard to take into account <u>all</u> the biological and chemical processes that influence climate. It can also be difficult to include <u>regional variations</u> in climate.

## Scientific Discoveries are **Communicated** to the **General Public**

Some scientific discoveries show that people should <u>change their habits</u>, or they might provide ideas that could be <u>developed</u> into new <u>technology</u>. So scientists need to <u>tell the world</u> about their discoveries.

<u>Gene technologies</u> are used in <u>genetic engineering</u> to produce <u>genetically modified crops</u>. Information about these crops needs to be communicated to <u>farmers</u> who might <u>benefit</u> from growing them and to the <u>general public</u>, so they can make <u>informed decisions</u> about the food they buy and eat.

## Scientific **Evidence** can be **Presented** in a **Biased Way**

1) Scientific discoveries that are reported in the <u>media</u> (e.g. newspapers or television) <u>aren't</u> peer-reviewed.

2) This means that, even though news stories are often <u>based</u> on data that has been peer-reviewed, the data might be <u>presented</u> in a way that is <u>over-simplified</u> or <u>inaccurate</u>, making it open to <u>misinterpretation</u>.

3) People who want to make a point can sometimes <u>present data</u> in a <u>biased way</u> (sometimes <u>without knowing</u> they're doing it). For example, a scientist might overemphasise a relationship in the data, or a newspaper article might describe details of data <u>supporting</u> an idea without giving any evidence <u>against</u> it.

## Companies can present biased data to help sell products...

Sometimes a company may only want you to see half of the story so they present the data in a <u>biased way</u>. For example, a pharmaceutical company may want to encourage you to buy their drugs by telling you about all the <u>positives</u>, but not report the results of any <u>unfavourable studies</u>.

# Issues Created by Science

Science has helped us <u>make progress</u> in loads of areas, from medicine to space travel. But science still has its <u>issues</u>. And it <u>can't answer everything</u>, as you're about to find out.

## Scientific Developments are Great, but they can Raise Issues

Scientific <u>knowledge is increased</u> by doing experiments. And this knowledge leads to <u>scientific developments</u>, e.g. new technologies or new advice. These developments can create <u>issues</u> though. For example:

> <u>Economic issues</u>: Society <u>can't</u> always <u>afford</u> to do things scientists recommend (e.g. investing in alternative energy sources) without <u>cutting back elsewhere</u>.

> <u>Social issues</u>: Decisions based on scientific evidence affect <u>people</u> — e.g. should alcohol be banned (to prevent health problems)? Would the effect on people's lifestyles be <u>acceptable</u>?

> <u>Personal issues</u>: Some decisions will affect <u>individuals</u>. For example, someone might support <u>alternative energy</u>, but object if a <u>wind farm</u> is built next to their house.

> <u>Environmental issues</u>: <u>Human activity</u> often affects the <u>natural environment</u>. For example, <u>genetically modified crops</u> may help us to produce <u>more food</u> — but some people think they could cause <u>environmental problems</u> (see p.69).

## Science Can't Answer Every Question — Especially Ethical Ones

1) We don't <u>understand everything</u>. We're always finding out <u>more</u>, but we'll never know <u>all</u> the answers.

2) In order to answer scientific questions, scientists need <u>data</u> to provide <u>evidence</u> for their hypotheses.

3) Some questions can't be answered <u>yet</u> because the data <u>can't</u> currently be <u>collected</u>, or because there's <u>not enough</u> data to <u>support</u> a theory.

4) <u>Eventually</u>, as we get <u>more evidence</u>, we'll answer some of the questions that <u>currently</u> can't be answered, e.g. what the impact of global warming on sea levels will be. But there will always be the "<u>Should we be doing this at all?</u>"-type questions that experiments <u>can't</u> help us to answer...

Think about <u>new drugs which can be taken to boost your 'brain power'</u>.
- Some people think they're <u>good</u> as they could improve concentration or memory. New drugs could let people think in ways beyond the powers of normal brains.
- Other people say they're <u>bad</u> — they could give some people an <u>unfair advantage</u> in exams. And people might be <u>pressured</u> into taking them so that they could work more <u>effectively</u>, and for <u>longer hours</u>.

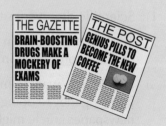

## There are often issues with new scientific developments...

The trouble is, there's often <u>no clear right answer</u> where these issues are concerned. Different people have <u>different views</u>, depending on their priorities. These issues are full of <u>grey areas</u>.

# Risk

Scientific discoveries are often great, but they can prove risky. With dangers all around, you've got to be aware of hazards — this includes how likely they are to cause harm and how serious the effects may be.

## Nothing is Completely Risk-Free

1) A hazard is something that could potentially cause harm.

2) All hazards have a risk attached to them — this is the chance that the hazard will cause harm.

3) The risks of some things seem pretty obvious, or we've known about them for a while, like the risk of causing acid rain by polluting the atmosphere, or of having a car accident when you're travelling in a car.

4) New technology arising from scientific advances can bring new risks, e.g. scientists are unsure whether nanoparticles that are being used in cosmetics and suncream might be harming the cells in our bodies. These risks need to be considered alongside the benefits of the technology, e.g. improved sun protection.

5) You can estimate the size of a risk based on how many times something happens in a big sample (e.g. 100 000 people) over a given period (e.g. a year). For example, you could assess the risk of a driver crashing by recording how many people in a group of 100 000 drivers crashed their cars over a year.

6) To make decisions about activities that involve hazards, we need to take into account the chance of the hazard causing harm, and how serious the consequences would be if it did. If an activity involves a hazard that's very likely to cause harm, with serious consequences if it does, that activity is considered high risk.

## People Make Their Own Decisions About Risk

1) Not all risks have the same consequences, e.g. if you chop veg with a sharp knife you risk cutting your finger, but if you go scuba-diving you risk death. You're much more likely to cut your finger during half an hour of chopping than to die during half an hour of scuba-diving. But most people are happier to accept a higher probability of an accident if the consequences are short-lived and fairly minor.

2) People tend to be more willing to accept a risk if they choose to do something (e.g. go scuba diving), compared to having the risk imposed on them (e.g. having a nuclear power station built next door).

3) People's perception of risk (how risky they think something is) isn't always accurate. They tend to view familiar activities as low-risk and unfamiliar activities as high-risk — even if that's not the case. For example, cycling on roads is often high-risk, but many people are happy to do it because it's a familiar activity. Air travel is actually pretty safe, but a lot of people perceive it as high-risk.

4) People may over-estimate the risk of things with long-term or invisible effects, e.g. ionising radiation.

## The pros and cons of new technology must be weighed up...

The world's a dangerous place and it's impossible to rule out the chance of an accident altogether. But if you can recognise hazards and take steps to reduce the risks, you're more likely to stay safe.

# Designing Investigations

Dig out your lab coat and dust off your badly-scratched safety goggles... it's <u>investigation time</u>.

## Evidence Can Support or Disprove a Hypothesis

1) Scientists <u>observe</u> things and come up with <u>hypotheses</u> to explain them (see p.2). You need to be able to do the same.  For example:

> <u>Observation:</u>  People with big feet have spots.  <u>Hypothesis:</u>  Having big feet causes spots.

2) To <u>determine</u> whether or not a hypothesis is <u>right</u>, you need to do an <u>investigation</u> to gather evidence.  To do this, you need to use your hypothesis to make a <u>prediction</u> — something you think <u>will happen</u> that you can test. E.g. people who have bigger feet will have more spots.

*Investigations include experiments and studies.*

3) Investigations are used to see if there are <u>patterns</u> or <u>relationships</u> between <u>two variables</u>, e.g. to see if there's a pattern or relationship between the variables 'number of spots' and 'size of feet'.

## Evidence Needs to be Repeatable, Reproducible and Valid

1) <u>Repeatable</u> means that if the <u>same person</u> does an experiment again using the <u>same methods</u> and equipment, they'll get <u>similar results</u>.

2) <u>Reproducible</u> means that if <u>someone else</u> does the experiment, or a <u>different</u> method or piece of equipment is used, the results will still be <u>similar</u>.

3) If data is <u>repeatable</u> and <u>reproducible</u>, it's <u>reliable</u> and scientists are more likely to <u>have confidence</u> in it.

4) <u>Valid results</u> are both repeatable and reproducible AND they <u>answer the original question</u>. They come from experiments that were designed to be a <u>FAIR TEST</u>...

## Make an Investigation a Fair Test By Controlling the Variables

1) In a lab experiment you usually <u>change one variable</u> and <u>measure</u> how it affects <u>another variable</u>.

2) To make it a fair test, <u>everything else</u> that could affect the results should <u>stay the same</u> — otherwise you can't tell if the thing you're changing is causing the results or not.

3) The variable you <u>CHANGE</u> is called the <u>INDEPENDENT</u> variable.

4) The variable you <u>MEASURE</u> when you change the independent variable is the <u>DEPENDENT</u> variable.

5) The variables that you <u>KEEP THE SAME</u> are called <u>CONTROL</u> variables.

> You could find how <u>temperature</u> affects the rate of an <u>enzyme-controlled reaction</u>. The <u>independent variable</u> is the <u>temperature</u>.  The <u>dependent variable</u> is the <u>rate of reaction</u>.  Control variables include the <u>concentration</u> and <u>amounts</u> of reactants, <u>pH</u>, the <u>time period</u> you measure, etc.

6) Because you can't always control all the variables, you often need to use a <u>control experiment</u>.  This is an experiment that's kept under the <u>same conditions</u> as the rest of the investigation, but <u>doesn't</u> have anything <u>done</u> to it.  This is so that you can see what happens when you don't change anything at all.

# Designing Investigations

## The **Bigger** the **Sample Size** the **Better**

1) Data based on <u>small samples</u> isn't as good as data based on large samples. A sample should <u>represent</u> the <u>whole population</u> (i.e. it should share as many of the characteristics in the population as possible) — a small sample can't do that as well. It's also harder to spot <u>anomalies</u> if your sample size is too small.

2) The <u>bigger</u> the sample size the <u>better</u>, but scientists have to be <u>realistic</u> when choosing how big. For example, if you were studying how <u>lifestyle</u> affects people's <u>weight</u> it'd be great to study everyone in the UK (a huge sample), but it'd take ages and cost a lot. It's more realistic to study a thousand people, with a <u>mixture</u> of ages, gender and race.

## Your **Equipment** has to be **Right for the Job**

1) The measuring equipment you use has to be <u>sensitive enough</u> to measure the changes you're looking for. For example, if you need to measure changes of 1 cm³ you need to use a <u>measuring cylinder</u> that can measure in <u>1 cm³</u> steps — it'd be no good trying with one that only measures 10 cm³ steps.

2) The <u>smallest change</u> a measuring instrument can <u>detect</u> is called its <u>resolution</u>. E.g. some mass balances have a resolution of 1 g, some have a resolution of 0.1 g, and some are even more sensitive.

3) Also, equipment needs to be <u>calibrated</u> by measuring a known value. If there's a <u>difference</u> between the <u>measured</u> and <u>known value</u>, you can use this to <u>correct</u> the inaccuracy of the equipment.

## Data Should be **Repeatable**, **Reproducible**, **Accurate** and **Precise**

1) To <u>check repeatability</u> you need to <u>repeat</u> the readings and check that the results are similar. You need to repeat each reading at least <u>three times</u>.

2) To make sure your results are <u>reproducible</u> you can cross check them by taking a <u>second set of readings</u> with <u>another instrument</u> (or a <u>different observer</u>).

3) Your data also needs to be <u>accurate</u>. Really accurate results are those that are <u>really close</u> to the <u>true answer</u>. The accuracy of your results usually depends on your <u>method</u> — you need to make sure you're measuring the right thing and that you don't <u>miss anything</u> that should be included in the measurements. E.g. estimating the <u>amount of gas</u> released from a reaction by <u>counting the bubbles</u> isn't very accurate because you might <u>miss</u> some of the bubbles and they might have different <u>volumes</u>. It's <u>more accurate</u> to measure the volume of gas released using a <u>gas syringe</u> (see p.148).

| Repeat | Data set 1 | Data set 2 |
|--------|------------|------------|
| 1 | 12 | 11 |
| 2 | 14 | 17 |
| 3 | 13 | 14 |
| Mean | <u>13</u> | <u>14</u> |

Data set 1 is more precise than data set 2.

4) Your data also needs to be <u>precise</u>. Precise results are ones where the data is <u>all really close</u> to the <u>mean</u> (average) of your repeated results (i.e. not spread out).

# Designing Investigations

## You Need to Look out for Errors and Anomalous Results

1) The results of your experiment will always <u>vary a bit</u> because of <u>random errors</u> — unpredictable differences caused by things like <u>human errors</u> in <u>measuring</u>. E.g. the errors you make when reading from a measuring cylinder are <u>random</u>. You have to <u>estimate</u> or <u>round</u> the distance when it's between two marks — so sometimes your figure will be a bit above the real one, and sometimes it will be a bit below.

2) You can <u>reduce</u> the effect of random errors by taking <u>repeat readings</u> and finding the <u>mean</u>. This will make your results <u>more precise</u>.

*If there's no systematic error, then doing repeats and calculating a mean could make your results more accurate.*

3) If a measurement is wrong by the <u>same amount every time</u>, it's called a <u>systematic error</u>. For example, if you measured from the very end of your ruler instead of from the 0 cm mark every time, all your measurements would be a bit small. Repeating the experiment in the exact same way and calculating a mean <u>won't</u> correct a systematic error.

4) Just to make things more complicated, if a systematic error is caused by using <u>equipment</u> that <u>isn't zeroed properly</u>, it's called a <u>zero error</u>. For example, if a mass balance always reads 1 gram before you put anything on it, all your measurements will be 1 gram too heavy.

5) You can <u>compensate</u> for some systematic errors if you know about them, e.g. if a mass balance always reads 1 gram before you put anything on it, you can subtract 1 gram from all your results.

6) Sometimes you get a result that <u>doesn't fit in</u> with the rest at all. This is called an <u>anomalous result</u>. You should investigate it and try to <u>work out what happened</u>. If you can work out what happened (e.g. you measured something wrong) you can <u>ignore</u> it when processing your results.

## Investigations Can be Hazardous

1) <u>Hazards</u> from science experiments might include:

- <u>Microorganisms</u>, e.g. some bacteria can make you ill.
- <u>Chemicals</u>, e.g. sulfuric acid can burn your skin and alcohols catch fire easily.
- <u>Fire</u>, e.g. an unattended Bunsen burner is a fire hazard.
- <u>Electricity</u>, e.g. faulty electrical equipment could give you a shock.

*You can find out about potential hazards by looking in textbooks, doing some internet research, or asking your teacher.*

2) Part of planning an investigation is making sure that it's <u>safe</u>.

3) You should always make sure that you <u>identify</u> all the hazards that you might encounter. Then you should think of ways of <u>reducing the risks</u> from the hazards you've identified. For example:

- If you're working with <u>sulfuric acid</u>, always wear gloves and safety goggles. This will reduce the risk of the acid coming into contact with your skin and eyes.
- If you're using a <u>Bunsen burner</u>, stand it on a heat proof mat. This will reduce the risk of starting a fire.

## Designing an investigation is an involved process...

Collecting <u>data</u> is what investigations are all about. Designing a good investigation is really important to make sure that any data collected is <u>accurate</u>, <u>precise</u>, <u>repeatable</u> and <u>reproducible</u>.

# Processing Data

Processing your data means doing some calculations with it to make it more useful.

## Data Needs to be Organised

1) Tables are really useful for organising data.

2) When you draw a table use a ruler and make sure each column has a heading (including the units).

## There are Different Ways of Processing Your Data

1) When you've done repeats of an experiment you should always calculate the mean (a type of average). To do this add together all the data values and divide by the total number of values in the sample.

2) You might also need to calculate the range (how spread out the data is). To do this find the largest number and subtract the smallest number from it.

*Ignore anomalous results when calculating the mean and the range.*

 **The results of an experiment to find the volume of gas produced in an enzyme-controlled reaction are shown below. Calculate the mean volume and the range.**

| Repeat 1 (cm³) | Repeat 2 (cm³) | Repeat 3 (cm³) | Mean (cm³) | Range (cm³) |
|---|---|---|---|---|
| 28 | 37 | 32 | (28 + 37 + 32) ÷ 3 = 32 | (37 − 28) = 9 |

3) You might also need to calculate the median or mode (two more types of average). To calculate the median, put all your data in numerical order — the median is the middle value. The number that appears most often in a data set is the mode.

*If you have an even number of values, the median is halfway between the middle two values.*

E.g. If you have the data set: 1 2 1 1 3 4 2
The median is: 1 1 1 2 2 3 4. The mode is 1 because 1 appears most often.

## Round to the Lowest Number of Significant Figures

The first significant figure of a number is the first digit that's not zero. The second and third significant figures come straight after (even if they're zeros). You should be aware of significant figures in calculations.

1) In any calculation where you need to round, you should round the answer to the lowest number of significant figures (s.f.) given.

2) Remember to write down how many significant figures you've rounded to after your answer.

3) If your calculation has multiple steps, only round the final answer, or it won't be as accurate.

 **A plant produces 10.2 cm³ of oxygen in 6.5 minutes whilst photosynthesising. Calculate the rate of photosynthesis.**

rate = 10.2 cm³ ÷ 6.5 min = 1.5692... = 1.6 cm³/min (2 s.f.)

        3 s.f.      2 s.f.    Final answer should be rounded to 2 s.f.

 **Don't forget your calculator...**

In the exam you could be given some data and be expected to process it in some way. Make sure you keep an eye on significant figures in your answers and always write down your working.

# Presenting Data

Once you've processed your data, e.g. by calculating the mean, you can present your results in a nice <u>chart</u> or <u>graph</u>. This will help you to <u>spot any patterns</u> in your data.

## Bar Charts Can be Used to Show Different Types of Data

Bar charts can be used to display:

1) <u>Categoric data</u> — data that comes in <u>distinct categories</u>, e.g. flower colour, blood group.

2) <u>Discrete data</u> — data that can be counted in <u>chunks</u>, where there's no in-between value, e.g. number of bacteria is discrete because you can't have half a bacterium.

3) <u>Continuous data</u> — <u>numerical data</u> that can have <u>any value</u> within a <u>range</u>, e.g. length, volume.

There are some <u>golden rules</u> you need to follow for <u>drawing</u> bar charts:

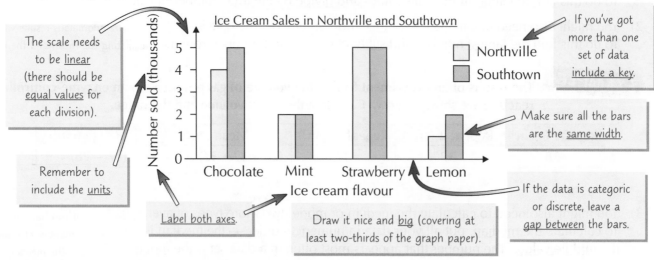

The scale needs to be <u>linear</u> (there should be <u>equal values</u> for each division).

If you've got more than one set of data <u>include a key</u>.

Make sure all the bars are the <u>same width</u>.

Remember to include the <u>units</u>.

<u>Label both axes</u>.

Draw it nice and <u>big</u> (covering at least two-thirds of the graph paper).

If the data is categoric or discrete, leave a <u>gap between</u> the bars.

## Graphs Can be Used to Plot Continuous Data

1) If both variables are <u>continuous</u> you should use a <u>graph</u> to display the data.

2) Here are the <u>rules</u> for plotting points on a graph:

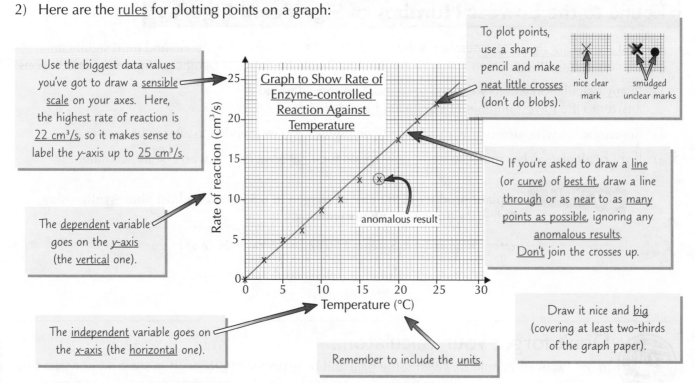

Use the biggest data values you've got to draw a <u>sensible scale</u> on your axes. Here, the highest rate of reaction is <u>22 cm³/s</u>, so it makes sense to label the y-axis up to <u>25 cm³/s</u>.

To plot points, use a sharp pencil and make <u>neat little crosses</u> (don't do blobs).

nice clear mark

smudged unclear marks

The <u>dependent</u> variable goes on the <u>y-axis</u> (the <u>vertical</u> one).

If you're asked to draw a <u>line</u> (or <u>curve</u>) of <u>best fit</u>, draw a line <u>through</u> or as <u>near</u> to as <u>many points as possible</u>, ignoring any <u>anomalous results</u>. <u>Don't</u> join the crosses up.

The <u>independent</u> variable goes on the <u>x-axis</u> (the <u>horizontal</u> one).

Remember to include the <u>units</u>.

Draw it nice and <u>big</u> (covering at least two-thirds of the graph paper).

# More on Graphs

Graph's aren't just fun to plot, they're also really useful for showing <u>trends</u> in your data.

## Graphs Can Give You a Lot of **Information** About Your **Data**

1) The <u>gradient</u> (slope) of a graph tells you how quickly the <u>dependent variable</u> changes if you change the <u>independent variable</u>.

$$\text{gradient} = \frac{\text{change in } y}{\text{change in } x}$$

The <u>graph</u> below shows the <u>volume of gas</u> produced in a reaction against <u>time</u>. The graph is <u>linear</u> (it's a straight line graph), so you can simply calculate the <u>gradient</u> of the line to find out the <u>rate of reaction</u>.

1) To calculate the gradient, pick <u>two points</u> on the line that are easy to read and a <u>good distance</u> apart.

2) <u>Draw a line down</u> from one of the points and a <u>line across</u> from the other to make a <u>triangle</u>. The line drawn down the side of the triangle is the <u>change in y</u> and the line across the bottom is the <u>change in x</u>.

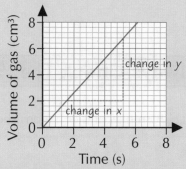

Change in y = 6.8 − 2.0 = 4.8 cm³   Change in x = 5.2 − 1.6 = 3.6 s

$$\text{Rate = gradient} = \frac{\text{change in } y}{\text{change in } x} = \frac{4.8 \text{ cm}^3}{3.6 \text{ s}} = \underline{1.3 \text{ cm}^3/\text{s}} \text{ or } \underline{1.3 \text{ cm}^3 \text{ s}^{-1}}$$

The units of the gradient are (units of y)/(units of x). cm³/s can also be written as cm³ s⁻¹.

*You can use this method to calculate any rates from a graph, not just the rate of a reaction. Just remember that a rate is how much something changes over time, so x needs to be the time.*

2) The <u>intercept</u> of a graph is where the line of best fit crosses one of the <u>axes</u>. The <u>x-intercept</u> is where the line of best fit crosses the x-axis and the <u>y-intercept</u> is where it crosses the <u>y-axis</u>.

## Graphs Show the **Relationship** Between Two Variables

1) You can get <u>three</u> types of <u>correlation</u> (relationship) between variables:

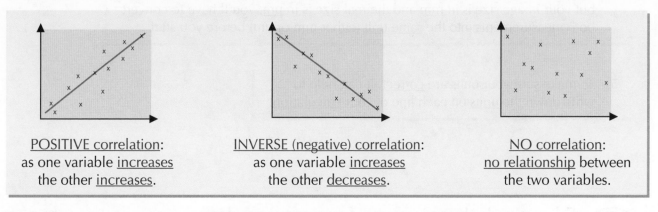

<u>POSITIVE correlation</u>: as one variable <u>increases</u> the other <u>increases</u>.

<u>INVERSE (negative) correlation</u>: as one variable <u>increases</u> the other <u>decreases</u>.

<u>NO correlation</u>: <u>no relationship</u> between the two variables.

2) Just because there's correlation, it doesn't mean the change in one variable is <u>causing</u> the change in the other — there might be <u>other factors</u> involved (see page 14).

# Units

Graphs and maths skills are all very well, but the numbers don't mean much if you don't get the <u>units</u> right.

## S.I. Units Are Used All Round the World

1) It wouldn't be all that useful if I defined volume in terms of <u>bath tubs</u>, you defined it in terms of <u>egg-cups</u> and my pal Fred defined it in terms of <u>balloons</u> — we'd never be able to compare our data.

2) To stop this happening, scientists have come up with a set of <u>standard units</u>, called S.I. units, that all scientists use to measure their data. Here are some S.I. units you'll see in biology:

| Quantity | S.I. Base Unit |
|----------|----------------|
| mass | kilogram, kg |
| length | metre, m |
| time | second, s |

## Always Check The Values Used in Equations Have the Right Units

1) Formulas and equations show <u>relationships</u> between <u>variables</u>.

2) To <u>rearrange</u> an equation, make sure that whatever you do to <u>one side</u> of the equation you also do to the <u>other side</u>.

For example, you can find the <u>magnification</u> of something using the equation: <u>magnification = image size ÷ real size</u> (see p.23). You can <u>rearrange</u> this equation to find the <u>image size</u> by <u>multiplying each side</u> by the real size: <u>image size = magnification × real size</u>

3) To use a formula, you need to know the values of <u>all but one</u> of the variables. <u>Substitute</u> the values you do know into the formula, and do the calculation to work out the final variable.

4) Always make sure the values you put into an equation or formula have the <u>right units</u>. For example, if you're calculating the magnification of something, but your image size is in <u>mm</u> and the real size is in <u>μm</u>, you'll have to convert both measurements into the <u>same unit</u> (either mm or μm) before you start.

5) To make sure your units are <u>correct</u>, it can help to write down the <u>units</u> on each line of your <u>calculation</u>.

## S.I. units help scientists to compare data...

You can only really <u>compare</u> things if they're in the <u>same units</u>. E.g. if the rate of blood flow was measured in ml/min in one vein and in l/day in another vein, it'd be hard to know which was faster.

# Converting Units

You can <u>convert units</u> using <u>scaling prefixes</u>. This can save you from having to write a lot of 0's...

## Scaling Prefixes Can Be Used for Large and Small Quantities

1) Quantities come in a huge <u>range</u> of sizes. For example, the volume of a swimming pool might be around 2 000 000 000 cm³, while the volume of a cup is around 250 cm³.

2) To make the size of numbers more <u>manageable</u>, larger or smaller units are used. These are the <u>S.I. base units</u> (e.g. metres) with a <u>prefix</u> in front:

| Prefix | tera (T) | giga (G) | mega (M) | kilo (k) | deci (d) | centi (c) | milli (m) | micro (μ) | nano (n) |
|---|---|---|---|---|---|---|---|---|---|
| Multiple of Unit | $10^{12}$ | $10^9$ | 1 000 000 ($10^6$) | 1000 | 0.1 | 0.01 | 0.001 | 0.000001 ($10^{-6}$) | $10^{-9}$ |

3) These <u>prefixes</u> tell you <u>how much bigger</u> or <u>smaller</u> a unit is than the base unit. So one <u>kilo</u>metre is <u>one thousand</u> metres.

4) To <u>swap</u> from one unit to another, all you need to know is what number you have to divide or multiply by to get from the original unit to the new unit — this is called the <u>conversion factor</u>.

*The conversion factor is the number of times the smaller unit goes into the larger unit.*

- To go from a <u>bigger unit</u> (like m) to a <u>smaller unit</u> (like cm), you <u>multiply</u> by the conversion factor.
- To go from a <u>smaller unit</u> (like g) to a <u>bigger unit</u> (like kg), you <u>divide</u> by the conversion factor.

5) Here are some conversions that'll be useful for GCSE biology:

Length can have lots of units including mm, μm and nm.

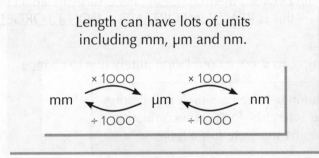

Mass can have units of kg and g.

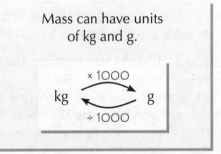

Volume can have units of m³, dm³ and cm³.

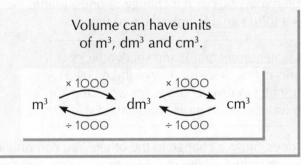

Time can have units of min and s.

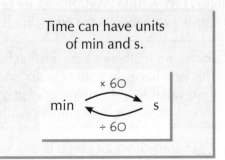

## To convert from bigger units to smaller units...

...<u>multiply</u> by the <u>conversion factor</u>, and to convert from <u>smaller units</u> to <u>bigger units</u>, <u>divide</u> by the <u>conversion factor</u>. Don't go getting this the wrong way round or you'll get some odd answers.

# Drawing Conclusions

Once you've carried out an experiment and processed your data, it's time to work out what your data shows.

## You Can **Only Conclude** What the Data Shows and **No More**

1) Drawing conclusions might seem pretty straightforward — you just look at your data and say what pattern or relationship you see between the dependent and independent variables.

The table on the right shows heights of pea plant seedlings grown for three weeks with different fertilisers.

| Fertiliser | Mean growth / mm |
|------------|------------------|
| A | 13.5 |
| B | 19.5 |
| No fertiliser | 5.5 |

CONCLUSION:
Fertiliser B makes pea plant seedlings grow taller over a three week period than fertiliser A.

2) But you've got to be really careful that your conclusion matches the data you've got and doesn't go any further.

You can't conclude that fertiliser B makes any other type of plant grow taller than fertiliser A — the results could be totally different.

3) You also need to be able to use your results to justify your conclusion (i.e. back up your conclusion with some specific data).

Over the three week period, fertiliser B made the pea plants grow 6 mm more on average than fertiliser A.

4) When writing a conclusion you need to refer back to the original hypothesis and say whether the data supports it or not:

The hypothesis for this experiment might have been that adding fertiliser would increase the growth of plants and that different types of fertiliser would affect growth by different amounts. If so, the data supports the hypothesis.

## Correlation DOES NOT Mean Cause

If two things are correlated (i.e. there's a relationship between them) it doesn't necessarily mean a change in one variable is causing the change in the other — this is REALLY IMPORTANT — DON'T FORGET it. There are three possible reasons for a correlation:

1) CHANCE: It might seem strange, but two things can show a correlation purely due to chance.

For example, one study might find a correlation between people's hair colour and how good they are at frisbee. But other scientists don't get a correlation when they investigate it — the results of the first study are just a fluke.

2) LINKED BY A 3RD VARIABLE: A lot of the time it may look as if a change in one variable is causing a change in the other, but it isn't — a third variable links the two things.

For example, there's a correlation between water temperature and shark attacks. This isn't because warmer water makes sharks crazy. Instead, they're linked by a third variable — the number of people swimming (more people swim when the water's hotter, and with more people in the water you get more shark attacks).

3) CAUSE: Sometimes a change in one variable does cause a change in the other. You can only conclude that a correlation is due to cause when you've controlled all the variables that could affect the result.

For example, there's a correlation between smoking and lung cancer. This is because chemicals in tobacco smoke cause lung cancer. This conclusion was only made once other variables (such as age and exposure to other things that cause cancer) had been controlled and shown not to affect people's risk of getting lung cancer.

# Uncertainty

Uncertainty is how sure you can really be about your data. There's a little bit of maths to do, and also a formula to learn. But don't worry too much — it's no more than a simple bit of subtraction and division.

## Uncertainty is the Amount of Error Your Measurements Might Have

1) When you repeat a measurement, you often get a slightly different figure each time you do it due to random error. This means that each result has some uncertainty to it.

2) The measurements you make will also have some uncertainty in them due to limits in the resolution of the equipment you use (see page 7).

3) This all means that the mean of a set of results will also have some uncertainty to it. You can calculate the uncertainty of a mean result using the equation:

$$\text{uncertainty} = \frac{\text{range}}{2}$$

 The range is the largest value minus the smallest value (see p.9).

4) The larger the range, the less precise your results are and the more uncertainty there will be in your results. Uncertainties are shown using the '±' symbol.

**EXAMPLE:**

**The table below shows the results of a respiration experiment to determine the volume of carbon dioxide produced. Calculate the uncertainty of the mean.**

| Repeat | 1 | 2 | 3 | mean |
|---|---|---|---|---|
| Volume of $CO_2$ produced (cm³) | 20.2 | 19.8 | 20.0 | 20.0 |

1) First work out the range:

Range = 20.2 − 19.8 = 0.4 cm³

2) Use the range to find the uncertainty:

Uncertainty = range ÷ 2 = 0.4 ÷ 2 = 0.2 cm³

So the uncertainty of the mean = 20.0 ± 0.2 cm³

5) Measuring a greater amount of something helps to reduce uncertainty.

For example, in a rate of reaction experiment, measuring the amount of product formed over a longer period compared to a shorter period will reduce the percentage uncertainty in your results.

## The smaller the uncertainty, the more precise your results...

Remember that equation for uncertainty. You never know when you might need it — you could be expected to use it in the exams. You need to make sure all the data is in the same units though. For example, if you had some measurements in metres, and some in centimetres, you'd need to convert them all into either metres or centimetres before you set about calculating uncertainty.

# Evaluations

Hurrah!  The end of another investigation.  Well, now you have to work out all the things you did <u>wrong</u>.
That's what <u>evaluations</u> are all about I'm afraid.  Best get cracking with this page...

## Evaluations — Describe **How** Investigations Could be **Improved**

An evaluation is a <u>critical analysis</u> of the whole investigation.

1)  You should comment on the <u>method</u> — was it <u>valid</u>?
    Did you control all the other variables to make it a <u>fair test</u>?

2)  Comment on the <u>quality</u> of the <u>results</u> — was there <u>enough evidence</u> to reach a
    valid <u>conclusion</u>?  Were the results <u>repeatable</u>, <u>reproducible</u>, <u>accurate</u> and <u>precise</u>?

3)  Were there any <u>anomalous</u> results?  If there were <u>none</u> then <u>say so</u>.
    If there were any, try to <u>explain</u> them — were they caused by <u>errors</u> in measurement?
    Were there any other <u>variables</u> that could have <u>affected</u> the results?
    You should comment on the level of <u>uncertainty</u> in your results too.

4)  All this analysis will allow you to say how <u>confident</u> you are that your conclusion is <u>right</u>.

5)  Then you can suggest any <u>changes</u> to the <u>method</u> that would <u>improve</u> the quality of the results,
    so that you could have <u>more confidence</u> in your conclusion.  For example, you might suggest
    <u>changing</u> the way you controlled a variable, or <u>increasing</u> the number of <u>measurements</u> you took.
    Taking more measurements at <u>narrower intervals</u> could give you a <u>more accurate result</u>.

    <u>Enzymes</u> have an <u>optimum temperature</u> (a temperature at which they <u>work best</u>).
    Say you do an experiment to find an enzyme's optimum temperature and take
    measurements at 10 °C, 20 °C, 30 °C, 40 °C and 50 °C.  The results of this experiment
    tell you the optimum is <u>40 °C</u>.  You could then <u>repeat</u> the experiment, <u>taking more
    measurements around 40 °C</u> to a get a <u>more accurate</u> value for the optimum.

6)  You could also make more <u>predictions</u> based
    on your conclusion, then <u>further experiments</u>
    could be carried out to test them.

*When suggesting improvements to the
investigation, always make sure that you say why
you think this would make the results better.*

## Always look for ways to improve your investigations

So there you have it — <u>Working Scientifically</u>.  Make sure you know this stuff like the back of your hand.
It's not just in the lab or the field, when you're carrying out your groundbreaking <u>investigations</u>, that you'll
need to know how to work scientifically.  You can be asked about it in the <u>exams</u> as well.  So swot up...

# Cells

When someone first peered down a microscope at a slice of cork and drew the <u>boxes</u> they saw, little did they know that they'd seen the <u>building blocks</u> of <u>every organism on the planet</u>...

## Organisms can be **Prokaryotes** or **Eukaryotes**

1) <u>All living things</u> are made of <u>cells</u>.

2) Cells can be either <u>prokaryotic</u> or <u>eukaryotic</u>. Eukaryotic cells are <u>complex</u> and include all <u>animal</u> and <u>plant</u> cells. Prokaryotic cells are <u>smaller</u> and <u>simpler</u>, e.g. bacteria (see next page).

*You might see the sizes of cells written in standard form — see p.24 for more on this.*

3) <u>Eukaryotes</u> are organisms that are made up of <u>eukaryotic cells</u>.

4) A <u>prokaryote</u> is a <u>prokaryotic cell</u> (it's a single-celled organism).

## **Plant** and **Animal** Cells have **Similarities** and **Differences**

### Animal Cells

*Subcellular structures are also known as organelles.*

The different parts of a cell are called <u>subcellular structures</u>. Most <u>animal</u> cells have the following subcellular structures — make sure you know them all:

<u>Nucleus</u> — contains <u>genetic material</u> that controls the activities of the cell. Genetic material is arranged into <u>chromosomes</u>.

<u>Cytoplasm</u> — gel-like substance where most of the <u>chemical reactions</u> happen. It contains <u>enzymes</u> (see page 26) that control these chemical reactions.

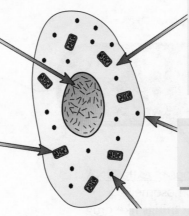

<u>Mitochondria</u> — these are where most of the reactions for <u>aerobic respiration</u> take place (see page 116). Respiration transfers <u>energy</u> that the cell needs to work.

<u>Cell membrane</u> — holds the cell together and controls what goes <u>in</u> and <u>out</u>.

<u>Ribosomes</u> — these are involved in <u>translation of genetic material</u> in the <u>synthesis of proteins</u>.

## Subcellular structures are all the different parts of a cell

Make sure you get to grips with the different <u>subcellular structures</u> that animal cells contain before you move on to the next page. There are more subcellular structures coming up that you <u>need to know</u>...

# Cells

## Plant Cells

Plant cells usually have <u>all the bits</u> that <u>animal</u> cells have,
plus a few <u>extra</u> things that animal cells <u>don't</u> have:

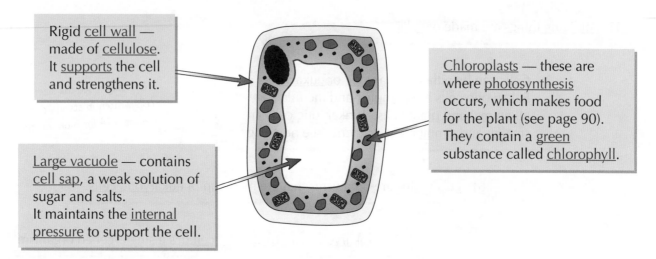

Rigid <u>cell wall</u> —
made of <u>cellulose</u>.
It <u>supports</u> the cell
and strengthens it.

Large vacuole — contains
<u>cell sap</u>, a weak solution of
sugar and salts.
It maintains the <u>internal</u>
<u>pressure</u> to support the cell.

Chloroplasts — these are
where <u>photosynthesis</u>
occurs, which makes food
for the plant (see page 90).
They contain a <u>green</u>
substance called <u>chlorophyll</u>.

## Bacterial Cells Have No Nucleus

<u>Bacterial cells</u> are a lot <u>smaller</u> than plant or animal cells and have these <u>subcellular structures</u>:

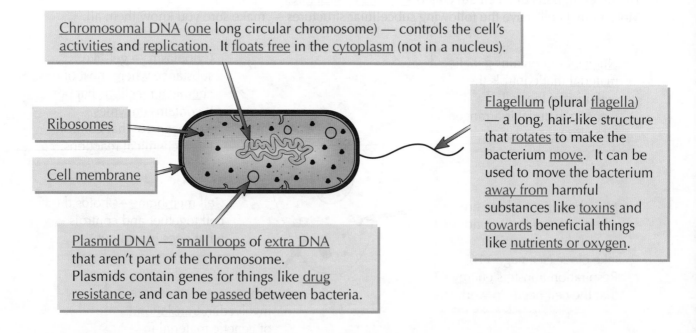

Chromosomal DNA (<u>one</u> long circular chromosome) — controls the cell's
<u>activities</u> and <u>replication</u>. It <u>floats free</u> in the <u>cytoplasm</u> (not in a nucleus).

<u>Ribosomes</u>

<u>Cell membrane</u>

Plasmid DNA — <u>small loops</u> of <u>extra</u> DNA
that aren't part of the chromosome.
Plasmids contain genes for things like <u>drug</u>
<u>resistance</u>, and can be <u>passed</u> between bacteria.

<u>Flagellum</u> (plural <u>flagella</u>)
— a long, hair-like structure
that <u>rotates</u> to make the
bacterium <u>move</u>. It can be
used to move the bacterium
<u>away from</u> harmful
substances like <u>toxins</u> and
<u>towards</u> beneficial things
like <u>nutrients or oxygen</u>.

## There's quite a bit to learn in biology — but that's life, I guess...

On these pages are a <u>typical animal cell</u>, <u>plant cell</u> and <u>bacterial cell</u>. Make sure you're
familiar with all their <u>structures</u>. A good way to check that you know what all the bits and pieces
are is to copy out the diagrams and see if you can remember all the labels. No cheating.

# Specialised Cells

The previous pages show the structure of some <u>typical cells</u>. However, most cells are <u>specialised</u> for a particular function, so their <u>structure</u> can vary...

## Different Cells Have Different Functions

1) <u>Multicellular organisms</u> contain lots of different <u>types</u> of cells (i.e. cells with different <u>structures</u>).

2) Cells that have a structure which makes them <u>adapted</u> to their function are called <u>specialised cells</u>.

3) You need to know how <u>egg</u>, <u>sperm</u> and <u>ciliated epithelial cells</u> are <u>adapted</u> to their functions.

## Egg Cells and Sperm Cells Are Specialised for Reproduction

1) In <u>sexual reproduction</u>, the <u>nucleus</u> of an egg cell <u>fuses</u> with the nucleus of a <u>sperm cell</u> to create a <u>fertilised egg</u>, which then develops into an <u>embryo</u>. Both the nucleus of an egg cell and of a sperm cell only contain <u>half</u> the number of chromosomes that's in a <u>normal</u> body cell — so they are called 'haploid'.

2) This is important as it means that when an egg and sperm nucleus <u>combine</u> at <u>fertilisation</u>, the resulting cell will have the <u>right number</u> of chromosomes.

There's more about sexual reproduction on page 49.

### Egg Cells

The main functions of an <u>egg</u> are to carry the female DNA and to <u>nourish</u> the developing embryo in the early stages. This is how it's adapted to its function:

1) It contains <u>nutrients</u> in the <u>cytoplasm</u> to feed the embryo.

2) It has a <u>haploid nucleus</u>.

3) Straight after <u>fertilisation</u>, its <u>membrane</u> changes <u>structure</u> to stop any more sperm getting in. This makes sure the offspring end up with the <u>right amount</u> of DNA.

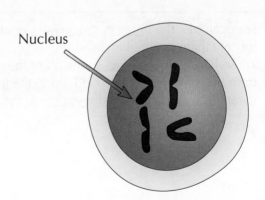

Nucleus

# Specialised Cells

## Sperm Cells

The <u>function</u> of a sperm is to <u>transport</u> the <u>male's DNA</u> to the <u>female's egg</u>.

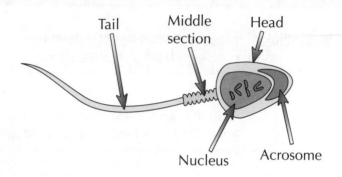

Tail    Middle section    Head

Nucleus    Acrosome

1) A sperm cell has a <u>long tail</u> so it can <u>swim</u> to the egg.

2) It has lots of <u>mitochondria</u> in the middle section to provide the <u>energy</u> (from respiration) needed to <u>swim</u> this distance.

3) It also has an <u>acrosome</u> at the front of the 'head', where it stores <u>enzymes</u> needed to <u>digest</u> its way through the <u>membrane</u> of the egg cell.

4) It also contains a <u>haploid nucleus</u>.

## Ciliated Epithelial Cells Are Specialised for Moving Materials

1) Epithelial cells <u>line the surfaces</u> of organs.

2) Some of them have <u>cilia</u> (hair-like structures) on the <u>top surface</u> of the cell.

3) The function of these <u>ciliated epithelial cells</u> is to <u>move substances</u> — the cilia beat to <u>move</u> substances in <u>one direction</u>, <u>along the surface</u> of the tissue.

For example, the <u>lining of the airways</u> contains <u>lots</u> of ciliated epithelial cells.
These help to move <u>mucus</u> (and all of the particles from the air that it has trapped) up to the <u>throat</u> so it can be <u>swallowed</u> and <u>doesn't reach</u> the lungs.

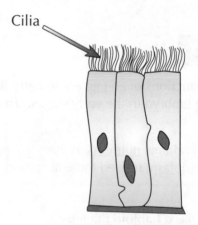

Cilia

## Cells have the same basic bits but are specialised for their function

Nearly every cell in your body is <u>specialised</u> to carry out some kind of function, but the ones on these pages — egg cells, sperm cells and ciliated epithelial cells — are the examples you need to <u>learn</u> for your exams.

# Microscopy

Without <u>microscopes</u> we would never have discovered cells. We can even use them to look <u>inside</u> cells.

## Cells are **Studied** Using **Microscopes**

Microscopes use lenses to <u>magnify</u> images (make them look bigger). They also increase the <u>resolution</u> of an image. <u>Resolution</u> means how well a microscope distinguishes between <u>two points</u> that are <u>close together</u>. A <u>higher resolution</u> means that the image can be seen <u>more clearly</u> and in <u>more detail</u>.

<u>Light microscopes</u> were invented in the 1590s. They work by passing <u>light</u> through the specimen. They let us see things like <u>nuclei</u> and <u>chloroplasts</u> and we can also use them to study <u>living cells</u>.

<u>Electron microscopes</u> were invented in the 1930s. They use <u>electrons</u> rather than <u>light</u>. Electron microscopes have a higher <u>magnification</u> and <u>resolution</u> than light microscopes, so they let us see much <u>smaller things</u> in <u>more detail</u> like the <u>internal structure</u> of mitochondria and chloroplasts. This has allowed us to have a much <u>greater understanding</u> of <u>how cells work</u> and the <u>role of subcellular structures</u> (although they can't be used to view living cells).

## You Can Create a **Scientific Drawing** of a **Specimen**

1) Using a <u>sharp</u> pencil, draw <u>outlines</u> of the <u>main features</u> using <u>clear, unbroken lines</u>. Don't include any <u>colouring</u> or <u>shading</u>.

2) Make sure that your drawing takes up <u>at least half</u> of the space available and remember to keep all the parts <u>in proportion</u>.

3) <u>Label</u> the <u>important features</u> of your diagram with <u>straight lines</u> which <u>don't cross over</u> each other, and include the <u>magnification</u> used and a <u>scale</u>.

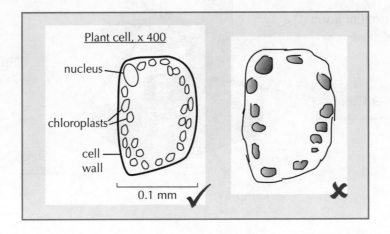

## Take your time when you're doing scientific drawings

When you look at a <u>real specimen</u> down a microscope, it often doesn't look exactly like what you'd expect from seeing diagrams in books. But don't be put off — just <u>draw what you can see</u>.

 **Microscopy**

It's all very well knowing what microscopes <u>do</u> — you also have to know how to actually <u>use</u> one.

## This is How to **View** a **Specimen** Using a **Light Microscope:**

1) Your specimen needs to <u>let light through it</u> so you'll need to take a <u>thin slice</u> of it to start with.

2) Next, take a clean <u>slide</u> and use a <u>pipette</u> to put one drop of water in the middle of it — this will <u>secure</u> the specimen in place. Then use <u>tweezers</u> to place your specimen on the slide.

3) Add a drop of <u>stain</u> if your <u>specimen</u> is completely <u>transparent</u> or <u>colourless</u> — this makes the specimen <u>easier to see</u> (different stains highlight different structures within cells, e.g. methylene blue stains DNA).

4) Place a <u>cover slip</u> at one end of the specimen, holding it at an <u>angle</u> with a <u>mounted needle</u> and carefully <u>lower</u> it onto the slide. Press it down <u>gently</u> so that no <u>air bubbles</u> are trapped under it. Then <u>clip</u> the slide onto the <u>stage</u>.

5) Select the <u>lowest-powered objective lens</u>.

6) Use the <u>coarse adjustment knob</u> to move the stage <u>up</u> so that the slide is <u>just underneath</u> the objective lens. Then, <u>looking</u> down the <u>eyepiece</u>, move the stage <u>downwards</u> (so you don't accidently crash it into the lens) until the specimen is <u>nearly in focus</u>.

7) Then <u>adjust the focus</u> with the <u>fine adjustment knob</u>, until you get a <u>clear image</u>. Position a <u>clear ruler</u> on the stage and use it to measure the <u>diameter</u> of the circular area visible — your <u>field of view</u> (<u>FOV</u>).

8) If you need to see your specimen with <u>greater magnification</u>, swap to a <u>higher-powered objective lens</u>, <u>refocus</u> and <u>recalculate</u> your <u>FOV</u> accordingly (e.g. if your FOV was 5 mm then you swap to a lens that is 10 times more powerful, your FOV will now be 5 mm ÷ 10 = 0.5 mm).

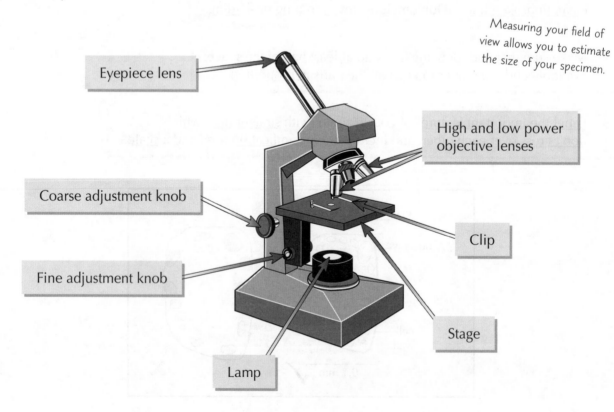

*Measuring your field of view allows you to estimate the size of your specimen.*

---

 ## Your microscope might look a bit different

The appearance of light microscopes can <u>vary</u> (e.g. they might have two eyepieces rather than one) but they should have the <u>same basic features</u> shown on this page.

# More Microscopy

Sometimes you need to do a bit of <u>maths</u> with microscope images.

## Magnification is **How Many Times Bigger** the Image is

1) If you know the <u>power</u> of the lenses used by a microscope to view an image, you can work out the <u>total magnification</u> of the image using this simple formula:

> **total magnification = eyepiece lens magnification × objective lens magnification**

 **An image is viewed with an eyepiece lens magnification of × 10 and an objective lens magnification of × 40. What is the total magnification?**

Total magnification = eyepiece lens magnification × objective lens magnification = 10 × 40 = × 400

2) If you don't know which lenses were used, you can still work out the magnification of an image as long as you can <u>measure the image</u> and know the <u>real size of the specimen</u>. This is the <u>formula</u> you need:

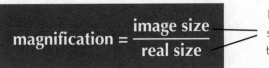
$$\text{magnification} = \frac{\text{image size}}{\text{real size}}$$

Both measurements should have the same units. If they don't, you'll need to convert them first (see next page).

 **A magnified image is 2 mm wide, and the specimen is 0.02 mm wide. What is the magnification?**

$$\text{magnification} = \frac{\text{image size}}{\text{real size}} = \frac{2}{0.02} = \times 100$$

3) If you're working out the <u>image size</u> or the <u>real size</u> of the object, you can rearrange the equation using this <u>formula triangle</u>. <u>Cover up</u> the thing you're trying to find. The parts you can <u>still see</u> are the formula you need to use.

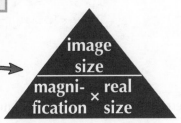

4) <u>Estimating</u> can help you to <u>check</u> that your answer is <u>correct</u>. To estimate an answer, <u>round</u> the numbers so you can do the maths in your <u>head</u>.

 **The real size of a specimen is 21.5 µm. The size of an image of the specimen is 9800 µm. Estimate the magnification used.**

1) First, <u>round</u> both numbers to <u>1 significant figure</u>.

   21.5 µm = 20 µm to 1 significant figure.
   9800 µm = 10 000 µm to 1 significant figure.

2) Then do the calculation.

   magnification = image size ÷ real size = 10 000 ÷ 20 = × 500

---

# More Microscopy

There's <u>more maths</u> coming up on this page — it might look a bit complicated, but really it's just a handy way of writing really small numbers a bit more neatly.

## You Might Need to Work in **Standard Form** and **Convert Units**

1) Because microscopes can see such <u>tiny objects</u>, sometimes it's useful to write figures in <u>standard form</u>.

2) This is where you change <u>very big</u> or <u>small</u> numbers with <u>lots of zeros</u> into something more manageable, e.g. 0.017 can be written $1.7 \times 10^{-2}$. To do this you just need to <u>move</u> the <u>decimal point</u> left or right.

3) The number of places the decimal point moves is then represented by a <u>power of 10</u> — this is <u>positive</u> if the decimal point's moved to the <u>left</u>, and <u>negative</u> if it's moved to the <u>right</u>.

4) You can also use <u>different units</u> to express very big or very small numbers. E.g. <u>0.0007 m</u> could be written as <u>0.7 mm</u>. The <u>table</u> shows you how to <u>convert between different units</u>. The right hand column of the table shows you how each unit can be expressed as a <u>metre</u> in <u>standard form</u>.

| To convert | Unit | To convert | In standard form: |
|---|---|---|---|
| × 1000 | Millimetre (mm) | ÷ 1000 | $\times 10^{-3}$ m |
| × 1000 | Micrometre (μm) | ÷ 1000 | $\times 10^{-6}$ m |
| × 1000 | Nanometre (nm) | ÷ 1000 | $\times 10^{-9}$ m |
| × 1000 | Picometre (pm) | | $\times 10^{-12}$ m |

So 1 pm = 0.000000000001 m.

Here's an example of a calculation in standard form:

**EXAMPLE:** A specimen is $5 \times 10^{-6}$ m wide. Calculate the width of the image of the specimen under a magnification of × 100. Give your answer in standard form.

1) <u>Rearrange</u> the magnification formula.     image size = magnification × real size

2) Fill in the <u>values</u> you know.     image size = 100 × ($5 \times 10^{-6}$ m)

3) Write out the values <u>in full</u> (i.e. don't use standard form).     = 100 × 0.000005 m

4) Carry out the calculation and then <u>convert back</u> into standard form.     = 0.0005 m     = $5 \times 10^{-4}$ m

0.0005 m could also be written as 0.5 mm or 500 μm.

## Make sure you pay close attention to the number of zeros

If you've got a <u>scientific calculator</u>, you can put <u>standard form</u> numbers into it using the 'EXP' or the '×10$^x$' button. For example, enter $2.67 \times 10^{15}$ by pressing 2.67 then 'EXP' or '×10$^x$', then 15.

# Warm-Up and Exam Questions

So, hopefully you've read the last eight pages. But could you cope if a question on cells or microscopes came up in the exam? With amazing new technology we can simulate that very situation...

## Warm-Up Questions

1) Name the subcellular structures where aerobic respiration takes place.
2) Give two ways that a sperm cell is adapted to its function.
3) What type of microscope should be used to look at the internal structure of chloroplasts?
4) Write the number 0.00045 μm in standard form.

## Exam Questions

1 Which of the following subcellular structures would you not expect to find in a prokaryotic cell?

☐ **A** plasmid ☐ **B** nucleus ☐ **C** cell wall ☐ **D** cell membrane

*[1 mark]*

2 **Figure 1** shows a typical plant cell.

(a) Which label points to a chloroplast?

☐ **A** ☐ **B** ☐ **C** ☐ **D**

*[1 mark]*

(b) Describe the function of a chloroplast.

*[1 mark]*

(c) **Figure 1** also shows ribosomes.
Describe the function of a ribosome.

*[1 mark]*

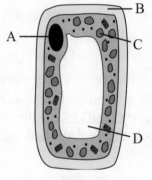

**Figure 1**

**PRACTICAL**

3 A light microscope can be used to observe a layer of onion cells on a slide.

(a)* Describe how you would use a light microscope to view onion cells.
Include how you would prepare the slide.

*[6 marks]*

(b) When the onion cell is viewed with × 100 magnification, the image of the cell is 7.5 mm wide.

Calculate the real width of the onion cell using the formula:

$$\text{magnification} = \frac{\text{image size}}{\text{real size}}$$

Give your answer in μm.

*[3 marks]*

# Enzymes

Chemical reactions are what make you work. And enzymes are what make them work.

## Enzymes Are Catalysts Produced by Living Things

1) Living things have thousands of different chemical reactions going on inside them all the time.

2) These reactions need to be carefully controlled — to get the right amounts of substances.

3) You can usually make a reaction happen more quickly by raising the temperature.
   This would speed up the useful reactions but also the unwanted ones too... not good.

4) So... living things produce enzymes which act as biological catalysts. Enzymes reduce the need for high temperatures and we only have enzymes to speed up the useful chemical reactions in the body.

> A CATALYST is a substance which INCREASES the speed of a reaction,
> without being CHANGED or USED UP in the reaction.

## Enzymes Have Special Shapes So They Can Catalyse Reactions

1) Chemical reactions usually involve things either being split apart or joined together.

2) The substrate is the molecule changed in the reaction.

3) Every enzyme has an active site — the part where it joins on to its substrate to catalyse the reaction.

4) Enzymes usually only work with one substrate. They are said to have a high specificity for their substrate.

5) This is because, for the enzyme to work, the substrate has to fit into the active site. If the substrate's shape doesn't match the active site's shape, then the reaction won't be catalysed. This is called the 'lock and key' mechanism, because the substrate fits into the enzyme just like a key fits into a lock.

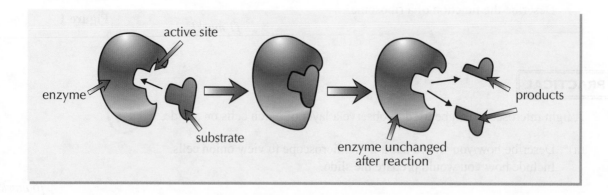

## Enzymes speed up chemical reactions

Just like you've got to have the correct key for a lock, you've got to have the right substance for an enzyme. If the substance doesn't fit into the active site, the enzyme won't be able to catalyse the reaction...

# Enzymes

Enzymes are clearly very clever, but they're <u>not</u> very versatile. They need just the right <u>conditions</u> if they're going to work properly.

## Enzymes Need the Right Temperature...

1) Changing the <u>temperature</u> changes the <u>rate</u> of an enzyme-catalysed reaction.

2) Like with any reaction, a higher temperature <u>increases</u> the rate at first.

3) But if it gets <u>too hot</u>, some of the <u>bonds</u> holding the enzyme together <u>break</u>. This changes the shape of the enzyme's <u>active site</u>, so the substrate <u>won't fit</u> any more. The enzyme is said to be <u>denatured</u>.

4) All enzymes have an <u>optimum temperature</u> that they work best at.

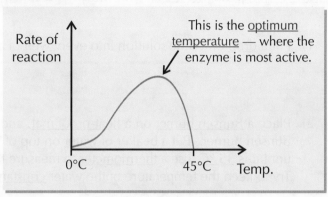

Enzymes denature at different temperatures. Most human enzymes denature at around 45 °C.

## ... and the Right pH...

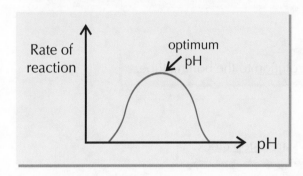

1) The <u>pH</u> also affects enzymes. If it's too high or too low, the pH interferes with the <u>bonds</u> holding the enzyme together.

2) This changes the <u>shape</u> of the <u>active site</u> and <u>denatures</u> the enzyme.

3) All enzymes have an <u>optimum pH</u> that they work best at. It's often <u>neutral pH 7</u>, but <u>not always</u> — e.g. <u>pepsin</u> is an enzyme used to break down <u>proteins</u> in the <u>stomach</u>. It works best at <u>pH 2</u>, which means it's well-suited to the <u>acidic conditions</u> there.

## ... and the Right Substrate Concentration

1) <u>Substrate concentration</u> also affects the rate of reaction — the higher the <u>substrate concentration</u>, the <u>faster the reaction</u>. This is because it's more likely that the enzyme will <u>meet up</u> and <u>react</u> with a substrate molecule.

2) This is only true <u>up to a point</u> though. After that, there are so many substrate molecules that the enzymes have about as much as they can cope with (<u>all the active sites are full</u>), and adding more makes <u>no difference</u>.

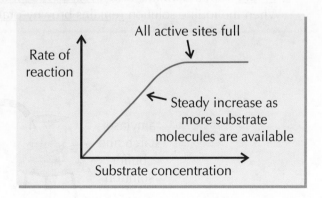

## Most enzymes catalyse just one reaction

The <u>optimum temperature</u> for most human enzymes is around <u>normal body temperature</u>. And <u>stomach enzymes</u> work best at <u>low pH</u>, but the enzymes in your <u>small intestine</u> like a <u>higher pH</u>.

# Investigating Enzyme Activity

## You Can **Investigate** the Effect of **pH** on **Enzyme Activity** | PRACTICAL

The enzyme <u>amylase</u> catalyses the breakdown of <u>starch</u> to <u>maltose</u>. It's easy to <u>detect starch</u> using <u>iodine</u> <u>solution</u> — if starch is present, the iodine solution will change from <u>browny-orange</u> to <u>blue-black</u>. This is how you can <u>investigate</u> how pH affects <u>amylase activity</u>:

1) Put a <u>drop</u> of iodine solution into every well of a <u>spotting tile</u>.

2) Place a <u>Bunsen burner</u> on a <u>heat-proof mat</u>, and a <u>tripod</u> and <u>gauze</u> over the Bunsen burner. Put a beaker of <u>water</u> on top of the tripod and <u>heat</u> the water until it is <u>35 °C</u> (use a <u>thermometer</u> to measure the temperature). Try to keep the temperature of the water <u>constant</u> throughout the experiment.

*You could use an electric water bath, instead of a Bunsen and a beaker of water, to control the temperature.*

3) Use a <u>syringe</u> to add 3 cm³ of <u>amylase solution</u> and 1 cm³ of a <u>buffer solution</u> with a pH of 5 to a boiling tube. Using <u>test tube holders</u>, put the tube into the beaker of water and wait for five minutes.

4) Next, use a <u>different syringe</u> to add 3 cm³ of a <u>starch solution</u> to the boiling tube.

5) Immediately <u>mix the contents</u> of the boiling tube and start a <u>stop clock</u>.

6) Use <u>continuous sampling</u> to record <u>how long</u> it takes for the amylase to break down all of the starch. To do this, use a dropping pipette to take a <u>fresh sample</u> from the boiling tube <u>every ten seconds</u> and put a <u>drop</u> into a <u>well</u>. When the iodine solution <u>remains browny-orange</u>, starch is no longer present.

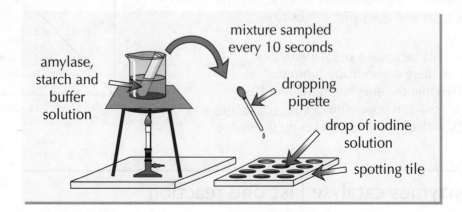

amylase, starch and buffer solution

mixture sampled every 10 seconds

dropping pipette

drop of iodine solution

spotting tile

# Investigating Enzyme Activity

7) <u>Repeat</u> the whole experiment with buffer solutions of different <u>pH values</u> to see how pH <u>affects</u> the time taken for the starch to be broken down.

*You could use a pH meter to accurately measure the pH of your solutions.*

8) Remember to <u>control any variables</u> each time (e.g. concentration and volume of amylase solution) to make it a <u>fair test</u>.

## Here's How to **Calculate** the **Rate of Reaction**

1) It's often useful to calculate the <u>rate of reaction</u> after an experiment. Rate is a measure of how much something changes over time.

2) For the <u>experiment above</u>, you can calculate the rate of reaction using <u>this formula</u>:

*You could also use the formula '1/time' but '1000/time' will give you a bigger number that's easier to plot on a graph.*

$$\text{Rate} = \frac{1000}{\text{time}}$$

E.g. at <u>pH 6</u>, the <u>time taken</u> for amylase to break down all of the starch in a solution was <u>90 seconds</u>. So the <u>rate</u> of the reaction = <u>1000 ÷ 90 = 11 s$^{-1}$</u> (2 s.f.)

*The units are in s$^{-1}$ since rate is given per unit time.*

3) If an experiment measures <u>how much something changes</u> over time, you calculate the rate of reaction by <u>dividing</u> the <u>amount</u> that it has <u>changed</u> by the <u>time taken</u>.

**EXAMPLE:** The enzyme catalase catalyses the breakdown of hydrogen peroxide into water and oxygen. During an investigation into the activity of catalase, 24 cm³ of oxygen was released in 50 seconds (s). Calculate the rate of the reaction. Write your answer in cm³ s$^{-1}$.

Amount of product formed = change = 24 cm³

Rate of reaction = change ÷ time
= 24 cm³ ÷ 50 s = 0.48 cm³ s$^{-1}$

*cm³ s$^{-1}$ is another way of writing cm³/s.*

## You can investigate other factors too...

You could easily <u>adapt</u> the experiment investigating amylase activity to see how factors <u>other than</u> pH affect the activity. For example, you could use a <u>water bath</u> to investigate the effect of <u>temperature</u>.

# Enzymes in Breakdown and Synthesis

Organisms use enzymes to help break down large molecules and to build them back up again.

## Enzymes Break Down Big Molecules

1) Proteins, lipids and some carbohydrates are big molecules.   Lipids are fats and oils.

2) It's important that organisms are able to break them down into their smaller components so they can be used for growth and other life processes.  For example:

   - Many of the molecules in the food we eat are too big to pass through the walls of our digestive system, so digestive enzymes break them down into smaller, soluble molecules. These can pass easily through the walls of the digestive system, allowing them to be absorbed into the bloodstream.  They can then pass into cells to be used by the body.
   - Plants store energy in the form of starch (a carbohydrate).  When plants need energy, enzymes break down the starch into smaller molecules (sugars).  These can then be respired to transfer energy to be used by the cells (see p.116).

## Different Enzymes Break Down Carbohydrates, Proteins and Lipids

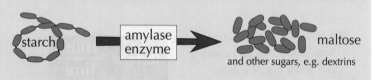

Enzymes called carbohydrases convert carbohydrates into simple sugars. E.g. amylase is an example of a carbohydrase.  It breaks down starch.

starch → amylase enzyme → maltose and other sugars, e.g. dextrins

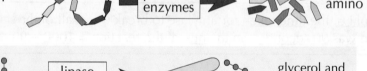

Proteases convert proteins into amino acids.

proteins → protease enzymes → amino acids

Lipases convert lipids into glycerol and fatty acids.

lipid → lipase enzymes → glycerol and fatty acids

When lipids are broken down, the fatty acids will lower the pH of the solution they are in.

## Some Enzymes Join Molecules Together

Organisms need to be able to synthesise carbohydrates, proteins and lipids from their smaller components. Again, enzymes are used in this process.

- Carbohydrates can be synthesised by joining together simple sugars.

  Glycogen synthase is an enzyme that joins together lots of chains of glucose molecules to make glycogen (a molecule used to store energy in animals).

- Proteins are made by joining amino acids together. Enzymes catalyse the reactions needed to do this.
- Lots of enzymes are also involved in the synthesis of lipids from fatty acids and glycerol.

## Different types of enzymes act on different molecules

Make sure you know all the smaller components that make up carbohydrates, proteins and lipids and understand that enzymes play a role in both the breakdown and synthesis of these bigger molecules.

# Warm-Up and Exam Questions

Doing well in exams isn't just about remembering all the facts, although that's important. You have to get used to the way the questions are phrased and make sure you always read the question carefully.

## Warm-Up Questions

1) What is meant by the term 'active site'?
2) What is meant by the optimum pH of an enzyme?
3) Name two other variables that affect the rate of enzyme activity.
4) Which enzyme breaks down:   (a) starch   (b) protein   (c) lipids?
5) What are the products of the breakdown of:   (a) starch   (b) protein
6) What type of molecule do enzymes join together to synthesise proteins?

## Exam Questions

1    **Figure 1** shows the effect of temperature on the action of two different enzymes.

(a)   Estimate the optimum temperature for enzyme **A**.

*[1 mark]*

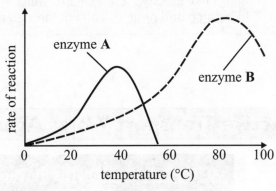

**Figure 1**

(b)   One of these enzymes was extracted from human liver cells. The other was extracted from bacteria living in hot underwater vents.

Suggest which enzyme came from the bacteria. Give a reason for your answer.

*[1 mark]*

**PRACTICAL**

2    A student was investigating the effect of pH on the rate of amylase activity. He used a syringe to put amylase solution and a buffer solution with a pH of 6 into a test tube. He then used a different syringe to add a starch solution to the boiling tube. He mixed the contents and then started a stop clock. Every 30 seconds he took a sample from the boiling tube and tested it for the presence of starch. When there was no starch present he stopped the stop clock. He repeated the experiment three times.

(a)   Suggest why he used two different syringes when adding substances to the boiling tube.

*[1 mark]*

(b)   His experiment showed that the average time taken for the starch in the boiling tube to be broken down was 60 seconds. Calculate the rate of the reaction. Give your answer in $s^{-1}$ to 2 significant figures. Use the formula:  $rate = \dfrac{1000}{time}$

*[1 mark]*

(c)   Suggest what the student needs to do next in his investigation to determine the effect of pH on the rate of amylase activity.

*[1 mark]*

# Diffusion and Active Transport

Substances can move in and out of cells by <u>diffusion</u> and <u>active transport</u>...

## Diffusion — Don't be Put Off by the **Fancy Word**

1) <u>Diffusion</u> is simple. It's just the <u>gradual movement</u> of particles from places where there are <u>lots</u> of them to places where there are <u>fewer</u> of them. That's all it is — just the <u>natural tendency</u> for stuff to <u>spread out</u>. Here's the fancy <u>definition</u>:

> <u>DIFFUSION</u> is the <u>net (overall) movement</u> of <u>particles</u> from an area of <u>higher concentration</u> to an area of <u>lower concentration</u>.

2) Diffusion happens in both <u>liquids</u> and <u>gases</u> — that's because the particles in these substances are free to <u>move about</u> randomly.

*If something moves from an area of higher concentration to an area of lower concentration it is said to have moved down a <u>concentration gradient</u>.*

3) Only very <u>small</u> molecules can <u>diffuse</u> through <u>cell membranes</u> — things like <u>glucose</u>, <u>amino acids</u>, <u>water</u> and <u>oxygen</u>. Big molecules like <u>starch</u> and <u>proteins</u> can't fit through the membrane.

## Active Transport Works **Against** a **Concentration Gradient**

> <u>ACTIVE TRANSPORT</u> is the <u>movement of particles</u> across a membrane against a concentration gradient (i.e. from an area of <u>lower</u> to an area of <u>higher concentration</u>) <u>using energy</u> transferred during respiration.

1) Active transport is a bit <u>different from diffusion</u> because particles are moved <u>up a concentration gradient</u> rather than down, and the process requires <u>energy</u> (unlike diffusion, which is a passive process).

2) Here's an example of active transport at work in the <u>digestive system</u>:

> When there's a <u>higher concentration</u> of nutrients in the gut than in the blood, the nutrients <u>diffuse naturally</u> into the blood.
>
> <u>BUT</u> — sometimes there's a <u>lower concentration</u> of nutrients in the gut than in the blood.
>
> Active transport allows nutrients to be taken into the blood, despite the fact that the <u>concentration gradient</u> is the wrong way. This is essential to stop us starving.

## Both processes involve movement between different concentrations

Make sure you understand the difference — in diffusion, particles passively move <u>down</u> a concentration gradient, whereas in active transport, particles move <u>up</u> a concentration gradient, which requires energy.

# Osmosis

If you've got your head round <u>diffusion</u>, osmosis will be a <u>breeze</u>.
If not, have another look at the previous page...

## Osmosis is a **Special Case** of **Diffusion,** That's All

<u>OSMOSIS</u> is the <u>net movement of water molecules</u> across a <u>partially permeable membrane</u> from a region of <u>higher water concentration</u> to a region of <u>lower water concentration</u>.

You could also describe osmosis as the net movement of water molecules across a partially permeable membrane from a region of <u>lower solute concentration</u> to a region of <u>higher solute concentration</u>.

1) A <u>partially permeable</u> membrane is just one with very small holes in it. So small, in fact, only tiny <u>molecules</u> (like water) can pass through them, and bigger molecules (e.g. <u>sucrose</u>) can't.

2) The water molecules actually pass <u>both ways</u> through the membrane during osmosis. This happens because water molecules <u>move about randomly</u> all the time.

3) But because there are <u>more</u> water molecules on one side than on the other, there's a steady <u>net flow</u> of water into the region with <u>fewer</u> water molecules, i.e. into the <u>more concentrated</u> solute solution.

4) This means the <u>solute</u> solution gets more <u>dilute</u>. The water acts like it's trying to "<u>even up</u>" the concentration either side of the membrane.

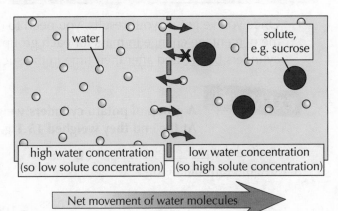

## You Can Do an **Experiment** to **Investigate Osmosis**    PRACTICAL

This experiment involves putting <u>potato cylinders</u> into <u>different concentrations</u> of <u>sucrose solution</u> to see what effect different <u>water concentrations</u> have on them.

The higher the concentration of the sucrose solution, the lower the water concentration.

### **First** You Do the Experiment...

1) Prepare <u>sucrose solutions</u> of different concentrations ranging from <u>pure water</u> to a <u>very concentrated sucrose solution</u>.

2) Use a cork borer to cut a <u>potato</u> into the <u>same sized pieces</u>. (The pieces need to be about <u>1 cm</u> in diameter and preferably from the <u>same potato</u>.)

3) Divide the cylinders into <u>groups of three</u> and use a <u>mass balance</u> to measure the <u>mass</u> of each <u>group</u>.

4) Place <u>one group</u> in each solution.

'M' is a unit of concentration (you might also see it written as mol dm$^{-3}$). The solution with a concentration of 0.0 M is pure water.

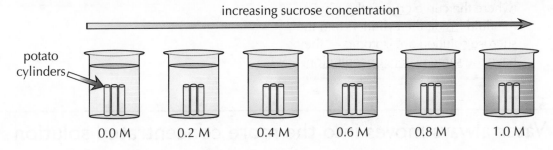

Topic 1 — Key Concepts in Biology

PRACTICAL

# Osmosis

5) <u>Leave</u> the cylinders in the solution for <u>at least 40 minutes</u> (making sure that they all get the <u>same amount</u> of time).

6) <u>Remove</u> the cylinders and <u>pat dry gently</u> with a paper towel. This removes <u>excess water</u> from the surface of the cylinders, so you get a more <u>accurate</u> measurement of their <u>final masses</u>.

7) <u>Weigh</u> each <u>group</u> again and record your results.

8) The <u>only</u> thing that you should <u>change</u> in this experiment is the <u>sucrose solution concentration</u>. Everything else (e.g. the volume of solution, the size of the potato cylinders, the type of potatoes used, the amount of drying, etc.) must be kept the <u>same</u> or your results <u>won't be valid</u>.

## ...Then You **Interpret** the **Results**

1) Once you've got all your results, you need to <u>calculate</u> the <u>percentage change in mass</u> for each group of cylinders <u>before</u> and <u>after</u> their time in the sucrose.

Calculating the percentage change allows you to compare the effect of sucrose concentration on cylinders that didn't have the same initial mass.

 EXAMPLE:

**A group of potato cylinders weighed 13.2 g at the start of the experiment. At the end they weighed 15.1 g. Calculate the percentage change in mass.**

To find the <u>percentage change in mass</u>, use the <u>formula</u> below:

$$\text{percentage change} = \frac{\text{final mass} - \text{initial mass}}{\text{initial mass}} \times 100$$

$$\text{percentage change} = \frac{15.1 - 13.2}{13.2} \times 100 = 14.4\%$$

The positive result tells you the potato cylinders gained mass. If the answer was negative then the potato cylinders lost mass.

2) Then you can plot a <u>graph</u> and <u>analyse your results</u>:

At the points <u>above</u> the x-axis, the water concentration of the <u>sucrose solutions</u> is <u>higher</u> than in the <u>cylinders</u>.
The cylinders <u>gain mass</u> as water is <u>drawn in</u> by osmosis.

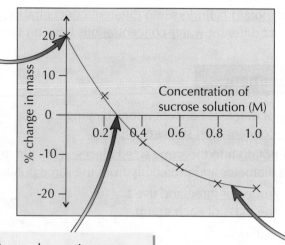

At the points <u>below</u> the x-axis, the water concentration of the <u>sucrose solutions</u> is <u>lower</u> than in the <u>cylinders</u>. This causes the cylinders to <u>lose water</u> so their mass <u>decreases</u>.

Where there is <u>no change</u> in mass (where the curve <u>crosses the x-axis</u>) the fluid <u>inside</u> the cylinders and the <u>sucrose solution</u> are <u>isotonic</u> — they have the <u>same water concentration</u>.

PRACTICAL TIP

## Water always moves into the more concentrated solution

This experiment used <u>sucrose</u> as a <u>solute</u>, but you could do it with <u>different solutes</u> (e.g. salt).

# Warm-Up and Exam Questions

Question time again — Warm-Up first, then Exam (or the other way round if you want to be different).

## Warm-Up Questions

1) Other than diffusion, by what two processes do substances move across cell membranes?
2) Give two differences between diffusion and active transport.
3) Explain what is meant by a partially permeable membrane.
4) What is the definition of osmosis?

## Exam Questions

**1**  A student adds a drop of ink to a glass of cold water.
Describe what you would expect to happen to the drop of ink.
Explain your answer.

*[2 marks]*

**PRACTICAL**

**2**  In an experiment, four 5 cm long cylinders were cut from a fresh potato.
The cylinders were then placed in different sugar solutions, as shown in **Figure 1**.
After 24 hours the potato cylinders were removed and measured.

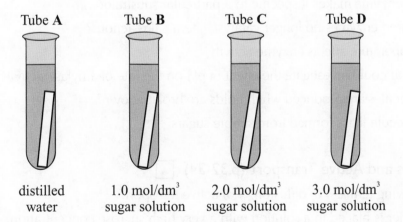

| Tube **A** | Tube **B** | Tube **C** | Tube **D** |
|---|---|---|---|
| distilled water | 1.0 mol/dm³ sugar solution | 2.0 mol/dm³ sugar solution | 3.0 mol/dm³ sugar solution |

**Figure 1**

(a)  State which potato cylinder you would expect to be shortest after 24 hours.
Explain your answer.

*[3 marks]*

(b)  The potato cylinder in tube **A** increased in length during the 24 hours.
Explain why this happened.

*[2 marks]*

# Revision Summary for Topic 1

Make sure you learn all of Topic 1 — many of the concepts will crop up again in other topics.

- Try these questions and tick off each one when you get it right.
- When you've done all the questions under a heading and are completely happy, tick it off.

## Cells and Specialised Cells (p.17-20) ☑

1) What is the function of the cell membrane? ☑
2) Give three structures found in plant cells but not in animal cells. ☑
3) Name the subcellular structures in plant cells where photosynthesis takes place. ☑
4) Name two structures that are found in both prokaryotic cells and eukaryotic cells. ☑
5) What does the term 'haploid' mean? ☑
6) Give three ways in which an egg cell is adapted to its function. ☑
7) What are cilia? ☑
8) What is the purpose of the ciliated epithelial cells that line the airways? ☑

## Microscopy (p.21-24) ☑

9) Give an advantage of electron microscopes over light microscopes. ☑
10) Why is it necessary to use thin samples of tissue when viewing cells using a light microscope? ☑
11) Write the equation you would use to find the size of a specimen using
the magnification used and the size of the image seen through a microscope lens. ☑
12) Describe how you would convert a measurement from mm to µm. ☑
13) Which unit can be expressed in standard form as $\times 10^{-12}$ m? ☑

## Enzymes (p.26-30) ☑

14) What part of an enzyme makes it specific to a particular substrate? ☑
15) Why can denatured enzymes no longer catalyse chemical reactions? ☑
16) Explain how temperature affects enzyme activity. ☑
17) Describe how you could investigate the effect of pH on the rate of amylase activity. ☑
18) Which two molecules are produced when lipids are broken down? ☑
19) Name a big molecule that's formed from simple sugars. ☑

## Diffusion, Osmosis and Active Transport (p.32-34) ☑

20) Define the following terms:   a) diffusion,   b) active transport. ☑
21) If a potato cylinder is placed in a solution with a very high sucrose concentration,
what will happen to the mass of the potato cylinder over time?  Explain why. ☑

# Mitosis

In order to survive and grow, our cells have got to be able to <u>divide</u>. And that means our DNA as well...

## Chromosomes Contain Genetic Information

1) Most cells in your body have a <u>nucleus</u>. The nucleus contains your <u>genetic material</u> in the form of <u>chromosomes</u>. Chromosomes are <u>coiled up</u> lengths of <u>DNA molecules</u> (see p.51 for more on DNA).

2) <u>Body cells</u> normally have <u>two copies</u> of each <u>chromosome</u> — this makes them 'diploid' cells. One chromosome comes from the organism's 'mother', and one comes from its 'father'.

3) When a cell divides by <u>mitosis</u> (see next page) it makes two cells <u>identical</u> to the original cell — the nucleus of each new cell contains the <u>same number of chromosomes</u> as the original cell.

## The Cell Cycle Makes New Cells for Growth and Repair

1) <u>Body cells</u> in <u>multicellular</u> organisms <u>divide</u> to produce new cells during a process called the <u>cell cycle</u>. The stage of the cell cycle when the cell divides is called <u>mitosis</u>.

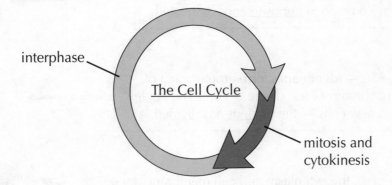

interphase

The Cell Cycle

mitosis and cytokinesis

2) Multicellular organisms use <u>mitosis</u> to <u>grow</u> or to <u>replace cells</u> that have been <u>damaged</u>.

3) Some organisms use mitosis to <u>reproduce</u> — this is called <u>asexual reproduction</u>. E.g. strawberry plants form runners by mitosis, which become new plants.

4) You need to know about the main stages of the <u>cell cycle</u>.

## Interphase

In a cell that's not dividing, the DNA is all spread out in <u>long strings</u>.

Before it divides, the cell has to <u>grow</u> and <u>increase</u> the amount of <u>subcellular structures</u> such as <u>mitochondria</u> and <u>ribosomes</u>.

It then <u>duplicates</u> its DNA — so there's one copy for each new cell. The DNA is copied and forms <u>X-shaped</u> chromosomes. Each 'arm' of the chromosome is an <u>exact duplicate</u> of the other.

The left arm of the chromosome has the same DNA as the right arm.

# Mitosis

## Mitosis and Cytokinesis

Once its contents and DNA have been copied, the cell is ready for <u>mitosis</u>.
Mitosis is divided into <u>four stages</u>:

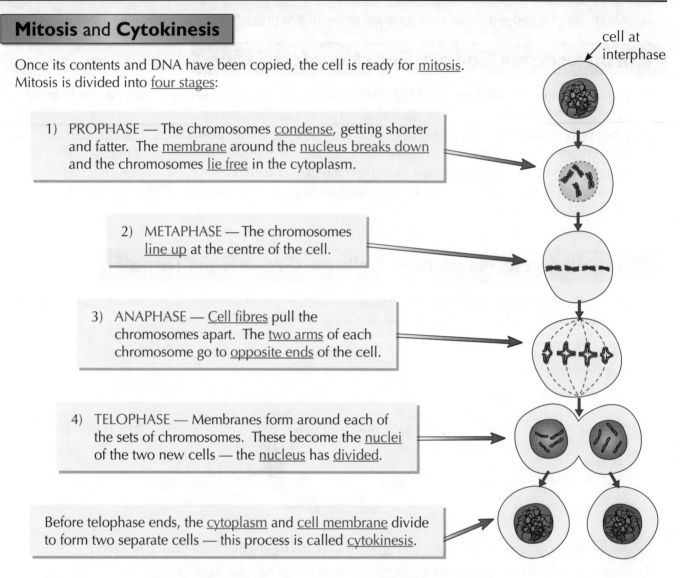

cell at interphase

1) PROPHASE — The chromosomes <u>condense</u>, getting shorter and fatter. The <u>membrane</u> around the <u>nucleus breaks down</u> and the chromosomes <u>lie free</u> in the cytoplasm.

2) METAPHASE — The chromosomes <u>line up</u> at the centre of the cell.

3) ANAPHASE — <u>Cell fibres</u> pull the chromosomes apart. The <u>two arms</u> of each chromosome go to <u>opposite ends</u> of the cell.

4) TELOPHASE — Membranes form around each of the sets of chromosomes. These become the <u>nuclei</u> of the two new cells — the <u>nucleus</u> has <u>divided</u>.

Before telophase ends, the <u>cytoplasm</u> and <u>cell membrane</u> divide to form two separate cells — this process is called <u>cytokinesis</u>.

At the end of mitosis, the cell has produced <u>two new daughter cells</u>. Each daughter cell contains exactly the <u>same sets of chromosomes</u> in its nucleus as the other daughter cell — they're <u>genetically identical diploid cells</u>. They're also genetically identical to the <u>parent cell</u>.

## You can Calculate the Final Number of Cells

You can <u>calculate</u> the <u>number of cells</u> there'll be after <u>multiple divisions</u> of a cell by mitosis. The formula you need is: <u>number of cells $= 2^n$</u>, where 'n' is the <u>number of divisions</u> by mitosis.

**EXAMPLE:**   **A cell divides by mitosis five times. How many cells are present after this process?**

Multiply <u>2</u> by itself for the number of <u>divisions</u> to find the number of <u>cells</u>.

$$2^5 = 2 \times 2 \times 2 \times 2 \times 2 = 32 \text{ cells}$$

## Mitosis produces two identical daughter cells

Mitosis can seem tricky at first. But don't worry — just go through it slowly, one step at a time.
This type of division produces <u>identical cells</u>, but there's another type which doesn't... (see page 50).

# Cell Division and Growth

Growth — it happens to us all. You need to know the <u>processes</u> involved in both <u>animal</u> and <u>plant</u> growth.

## Growth Involves Cell Division, Differentiation and Elongation

<u>Growth</u> is an <u>increase</u> in <u>size</u> or <u>mass</u>. Plants and animals <u>grow</u> and <u>develop</u> due to these processes:

- <u>CELL DIFFERENTIATION</u> — the process by which a cell <u>changes</u> to become <u>specialised</u> for its <u>job</u>. Having specialised cells allows multicellular organisms to work more <u>efficiently</u>.

  *See pages 19-20 for more on specialised cells.*

- <u>CELL DIVISION</u> — by <u>mitosis</u> (see pages 37-38).

- <u>Plants</u> also grow by <u>CELL ELONGATION</u>. This is where a plant cell <u>expands</u>, making the cell <u>bigger</u> and so making the plant <u>grow</u>.

### Animals

1) <u>All growth</u> in <u>animals</u> happens by <u>cell division</u>.
2) Animals tend to grow while they're <u>young</u>, and then they reach <u>full growth</u> and <u>stop</u> growing.
3) So when you're young, cells divide at a <u>fast rate</u> but once you're an adult, most cell division is for <u>repair</u> — the cells divide to <u>replace</u> old or damaged cells.
4) This also means, in most animals, <u>cell differentiation</u> is <u>lost</u> at an <u>early stage</u>.

### Plants

1) In <u>plants</u>, growth in <u>height</u> is mainly due to cell <u>elongation</u> — cell <u>division</u> usually just happens in the <u>tips</u> of the <u>roots</u> and <u>shoots</u> (in areas called meristems — see page 41).
2) But <u>plants</u> often grow <u>continuously</u> — even really old trees will keep putting out <u>new branches</u>. So, plants continue to <u>differentiate</u> to <u>develop new parts</u>, e.g. leaves, roots.

## Cancer is a Case of Uncontrolled Cell Division

1) The <u>rate</u> at which <u>cells divide</u> by <u>mitosis</u> is controlled by the chemical instructions (<u>genes</u>) in an organism's DNA.
2) If there's a <u>change</u> in one of the genes that controls cell division, the cell may start dividing <u>uncontrollably</u>.
3) This can result in a <u>mass of abnormal cells</u> called a <u>tumour</u>.
4) If the tumour <u>invades and destroys</u> surrounding tissue it is called <u>cancer</u>.

*A random change in a gene is called a mutation — see page 59.*

---

## Growth is different in plants and animals...

Remember, both plant and animals grow by <u>cell differentiation</u> and <u>cell division</u>, but plants use <u>cell elongation</u> too. Plants <u>continue to grow</u> throughout their lives too, but animals <u>stop growing</u> once they reach full size.

Topic 2 — Cells and Control

# Percentile Charts

It's important to <u>monitor growth</u> in children — there's a certain type of <u>graph</u> that can be used for this...

## Percentile Charts are Used to Monitor Growth

1) <u>Growth charts</u> are used to assess a <u>child's growth</u> over time, so that an <u>overall pattern in development</u> can be seen and any <u>problems highlighted</u> (e.g. obesity, malnutrition, dwarfism).

2) For example, a baby's growth is regularly <u>monitored</u> after birth to make sure it's growing <u>normally</u>. Three measurements are taken — <u>length</u>, <u>mass</u> and <u>head circumference</u>.

3) These results are plotted on <u>growth charts</u>, like the one below.

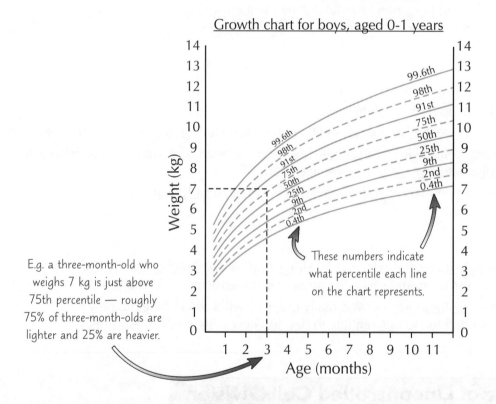

Growth chart for boys, aged 0-1 years

These numbers indicate what percentile each line on the chart represents.

E.g. a three-month-old who weighs 7 kg is just above 75th percentile — roughly 75% of three-month-olds are lighter and 25% are heavier.

4) The chart shows a number of '<u>percentiles</u>'. E.g. the <u>50th percentile</u> shows the mass that <u>50%</u> of babies will have reached at a certain age.

5) Babies <u>vary</u> in size, but doctors are likely to investigate if a baby's size is above the <u>top</u> percentile line or below the <u>bottom</u> percentile line, their size increases or decreases by <u>two or more</u> percentile lines over time, or if there's an <u>inconsistent pattern</u> (e.g. a small baby with a very large head).

## Percentile charts show the distribution of sizes in a population

<u>Percentiles</u> tell you <u>where</u> in the data set a data point lies. The <u>value</u> of a percentile tells you what <u>percentage</u> of data has a value <u>equal to or lower than</u> the data points in that percentile.

# Stem Cells

Your body is made up of <u>all sorts</u> of cells — this page tells you where they all <u>came from</u>.

## Stem Cells can Differentiate into Different Types of Cells

1) As you saw on page 39, cells <u>differentiate</u> to become <u>specialised cells</u>.

2) <u>Undifferentiated</u> cells are called <u>stem cells</u>.

3) Depending on what instructions they're given, stem cells can <u>divide</u> by <u>mitosis</u> to become <u>new cells</u>, which then <u>differentiate</u>.

4) Stem cells are found in early <u>human embryos</u>. These embryonic stem cells have the potential to divide and produce <u>any</u> kind of cell at all. This makes sense — <u>all</u> the <u>different types</u> of cell found in a human have to come from those <u>few cells</u> in the early embryo.

5) This means stem cells are really important for the <u>growth</u> and <u>development</u> of organisms.

6) <u>Adults</u> also have stem cells, but they're only found in certain places, like <u>bone marrow</u>. These aren't as <u>versatile</u> as embryonic stem cells — they can't produce <u>any</u> cell type at all, only certain ones. In animals, adult stem cells are used to <u>replace damaged cells</u>, e.g. to make new skin or blood cells.

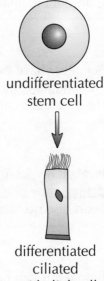

undifferentiated
stem cell

differentiated
ciliated
epithelial cell
(see p.20)

## Meristems Contain Plant Stem Cells

In plants, the only cells that <u>divide by mitosis</u> are found in plant tissues called <u>meristems</u>.

1) Meristem tissue is found in the areas of a plant that are <u>growing</u>, e.g. the tips of the <u>roots and shoots</u>.

2) Meristems produce <u>unspecialised cells</u> that are able to divide and form <u>any cell type</u> in the plant — they act like <u>embryonic stem cells</u>. But unlike human stem cells, these cells can <u>divide</u> and <u>differentiate</u> to generate any type of cell <u>for as long as the plant lives</u>.

3) The <u>unspecialised cells</u> go on to form <u>specialised tissues</u> like <u>xylem</u> and <u>phloem</u> (see p.94).

## Embryonic stem cells can become any type of cell

Unspecialised cells produced by plant meristems can differentiate into <u>any type</u> of cell so that the plant can <u>continue to grow</u>. Because humans <u>stop growing</u>, adult stem cells only differentiate into certain cell types.

# Stem Cells

Stem cell research has exciting <u>possibilities</u>, but it's also pretty <u>controversial</u>.

## Stem Cells Can be **Used in Medicine**

1) Doctors already use <u>adult stem cells</u> to cure some <u>diseases</u>.
E.g. <u>sickle cell anaemia</u> can sometimes be cured with a <u>bone marrow transplant</u> (containing adult stem cells which produce new blood cells).

2) Scientists have experimented with <u>extracting stem cells</u> from very early <u>human embryos</u> and <u>growing</u> them. Under certain conditions the stem cells can be stimulated to differentiate into <u>specialised cells</u>.

3) It might be possible to use stem cells to create specialised cells to <u>replace</u> those which have been <u>damaged</u> by <u>disease</u> or <u>injury</u>, e.g. new cardiac muscle cells could be <u>transplanted</u> into someone with heart disease. This <u>potential</u> for <u>new cures</u> is the reason for the huge scientific interest in stem cells.

4) Before this can happen, a lot of <u>research</u> needs to be done. There are many <u>potential risks</u> which scientists need to learn more about. For example:

### Rejection

If the transplanted cells aren't grown using the patient's own stem cells, the patient's body may recognise the cells as <u>foreign</u> and trigger an <u>immune response</u> to try to get rid of them.
The patient can take <u>drugs</u> to <u>suppress</u> this response, but this makes them <u>susceptible</u> to <u>diseases</u>.

### Tumour development

Stem cells <u>divide</u> very <u>quickly</u>. If scientists are <u>unable to control the rate</u> at which the transplanted cells divide inside a patient, a <u>tumour</u> may develop (see page 39).

### Disease transmission

<u>Viruses</u> live inside cells. If donor stem cells are infected with a virus and this isn't picked up, the virus could be <u>passed on</u> to the recipient and so make them <u>sicker</u>.

5) Research using embryonic stem cells raises <u>ethical issues</u>. E.g. some people argue that human embryos <u>shouldn't</u> be used for experiments because each one is a <u>potential human life</u>. But others think that the aim of <u>curing patients</u> who are <u>suffering</u> should be <u>more important</u> than the potential life of the embryos.

## Stem cells could help cure many diseases in the future

Questions on the <u>issues</u> associated with using stem cells in <u>medicine</u> might crop up in the exam, so make sure you know the <u>potential benefits</u> and the <u>risks</u> associated with using them.

# Warm-Up and Exam Questions

Here's a page of questions — use them to help you brush up your 'cell division and growth' knowledge.

## Warm-Up Questions

1) What does cell 'differentiation' mean?
2) True or false?  Plants can grow by cell elongation.
3) What does it mean if the weight of a two-month-old baby is at the 25th percentile on a growth chart?
4) Where in the cell are chromosomes found?

## Exam Questions

**1**  **Figure 1** shows how the amount of DNA per cell changes as a cell undergoes two cell divisions by mitosis.  Point **C** is the time when the chromosomes first become visible in the cells.

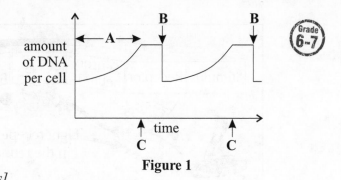
**Figure 1**

(a)  Describe what is happening to the DNA during stage **A**. Suggest why this needs to happen.

*[2 marks]*

(b)  Suggest what happens at time **B**.

*[1 mark]*

(c)  State how many cells there are after the first cell division.

*[1 mark]*

(d)  Cancer is a disease caused by problems in the cell division process. Describe how changes in cells can lead to cancer.

*[2 marks]*

**2**  Adult stem cells have already been used to cure disorders, and it is thought that embryonic stem cells have the potential to treat many more disorders.

(a)  Describe how embryonic stem cells could be used to treat disorders.

*[1 mark]*

(b)  Explain why embryonic stem cells have the potential to treat more disorders than adult stem cells.

*[1 mark]*

**3**  A bacterial cell divides once every 30 minutes. Calculate the number of cells that will be present after 3 hours.

*[2 marks]*

# The Nervous System

The <u>nervous system</u> means that humans can <u>react to their surroundings</u> and <u>coordinate their behaviour</u>.

## The **Central Nervous System (CNS) Coordinates** a **Response**

1) The nervous system is made up of <u>neurones</u> (nerve cells) which go to <u>all parts</u> of the body.

2) The body has lots of sensory <u>receptors</u> — groups of <u>cells</u> that can detect a <u>change in your environment</u> (a <u>stimulus</u>). Different receptors detect different stimuli. For example, receptors in your <u>eyes</u> detect <u>light</u>, while receptors in your <u>skin</u> detect <u>touch</u> (pressure) and <u>temperature change</u>.

3) When a <u>stimulus</u> is detected by <u>receptors</u>, the information is <u>converted</u> to a <u>nervous (electrical) impulse</u> and sent along <u>sensory neurones</u> to the <u>CNS</u> (the brain and spinal cord).

4) The CNS <u>coordinates</u> the response (in other words, it <u>decides what to do</u> about the stimulus and tells something to do it). Impulses travel through the CNS along <u>relay neurones</u>.

5) The CNS sends information to an <u>effector</u> (<u>muscle</u> or <u>gland</u>) along a <u>motor neurone</u>. The effector then <u>responds</u> accordingly — e.g. a <u>muscle</u> may <u>contract</u> or a <u>gland</u> may <u>secrete a hormone</u>.

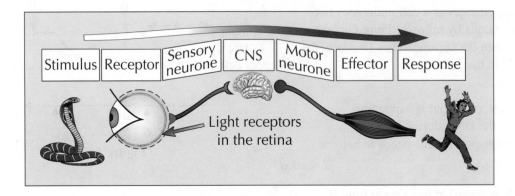

| Stimulus | Receptor | Sensory neurone | CNS | Motor neurone | Effector | Response |

Light receptors in the retina

6) The <u>time</u> it takes you to <u>respond</u> to a stimulus is called your <u>reaction time</u>.

## **Neurones** Transmit Information **Rapidly** as **Electrical Impulses**

1) All neurones have a <u>cell body</u> with a <u>nucleus</u> (plus cytoplasm and other subcellular structures).

2) The cell body has <u>extensions</u> that <u>connect to other neurones</u> — <u>dendrites</u> and <u>dendrons</u> carry nerve impulses <u>towards</u> the cell body, and <u>axons</u> carry nerve impulses <u>away</u> from the cell body.

3) Some axons are surrounded by a <u>myelin sheath</u>. This acts as an <u>electrical insulator</u>, <u>speeding up</u> the electrical impulse.

4) Neurones can be very <u>long</u>, which also <u>speeds up</u> the impulse (<u>connecting</u> with <u>another neurone</u> slows the impulse down, so one long neurone is much <u>quicker</u> than lots of short ones joined together).

*There's more on axons and dendrites on the next page.*

---

**EXAM TIP**

## The exam isn't just a test of what you know...

...it's also a test of how well you can <u>apply</u> what you know. For instance, you might have to take what you know about a <u>human's nervous system</u> and apply it to a <u>horse</u>. The key is <u>not to panic</u> — just <u>think carefully</u> about the information that you are given.

# The Nervous System

## There are **Different Types** of **Neurones**

You need to know the structure and function of sensory, motor and relay neurones.

### Sensory Neurone

1) One long dendron carries nerve impulses from receptor cells to the cell body, which is located in the middle of the neurone.

2) One short axon carries nerve impulses from the cell body to the CNS.

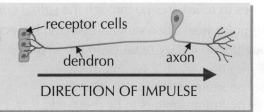
receptor cells
dendron
axon
DIRECTION OF IMPULSE

### Motor Neurone

1) Many short dendrites carry nerve impulses from the CNS to the cell body.

2) One long axon carries nerve impulses from the cell body to effector cells.

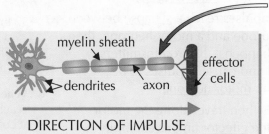
myelin sheath
effector cells
dendrites
axon
DIRECTION OF IMPULSE

*The diagram shows a myelinated motor neurone but you can get unmyelinated ones too. Sensory and relay neurones can also be myelinated.*

### Relay Neurone

1) Many short dendrites carry nerve impulses from sensory neurones to the cell body.

2) An axon carries nerve impulses from the cell body to motor neurones.

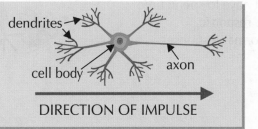
dendrites
cell body
axon
DIRECTION OF IMPULSE

## Synapses Connect Neurones

1) The connection between two neurones is called a synapse.

2) The nerve signal is transferred by chemicals called neurotransmitters, which diffuse (move) across the gap.

3) The neurotransmitters then set off a new electrical signal in the next neurone.

4) The transmission of a nervous impulse is very fast, but it is slowed down a bit at the synapse because the diffusion of neurotransmitters across the gap takes time.

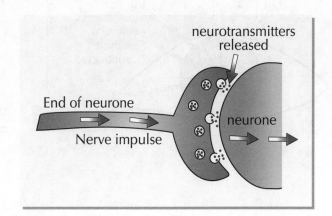
neurotransmitters released
End of neurone
Nerve impulse
neurone

---

REVISION TIP

## Make sure you know the differences between the neurones

You need to know the structures and functions of the different types of neurones — try drawing out the diagrams yourself and putting annotations on them saying what each part does.

# Reflexes

Sometimes you respond to a stimulus <u>without thinking</u> about it — this is a <u>reflex</u>.

## Reflexes Help Prevent Injury

1) <u>Reflexes</u> are <u>automatic</u>, <u>rapid</u> responses to stimuli — they can reduce the chances of being injured.

2) The passage of information in a reflex (from receptor to effector) is called a <u>reflex arc</u>.

3) The neurones in reflex arcs go through the <u>spinal cord</u> or through an <u>unconscious part of the brain</u>.

4) When a <u>stimulus</u> (e.g. a bee sting) is detected by receptors, <u>impulses</u> are sent along a <u>sensory neurone</u> to a <u>relay neurone</u> in the CNS.

5) When the impulses reach a <u>synapse</u> between the sensory neurone and the relay neurone, they trigger <u>neurotransmitters</u> to be released (see previous page). These cause impulses to be sent along the <u>relay neurone</u>.

6) When the impulses reach a <u>synapse</u> between the relay neurone and a motor neurone, the same thing happens. Neurotransmitters are released and cause impulses to be sent along the <u>motor neurone</u>.

7) The impulses then travel along the motor neurone to the <u>effector</u> (in this example it's a muscle, but it could be a gland).

8) The <u>muscle</u> then <u>contracts</u> and moves your hand away from the bee.

9) Because you don't have to spend time thinking about the response, it's <u>quicker</u> than normal responses.

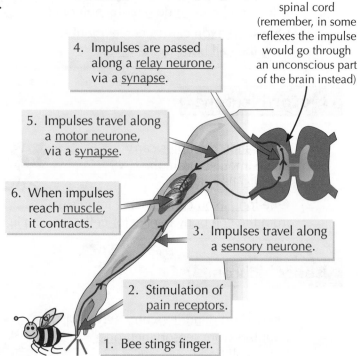

spinal cord (remember, in some reflexes the impulse would go through an unconscious part of the brain instead)

4. Impulses are passed along a <u>relay neurone</u>, via a <u>synapse</u>.

5. Impulses travel along a <u>motor neurone</u>, via a <u>synapse</u>.

6. When impulses reach <u>muscle</u>, it contracts.

3. Impulses travel along a <u>sensory neurone</u>.

2. Stimulation of <u>pain receptors</u>.

1. Bee stings finger.

## A Reflex Helps to Protect the Eye

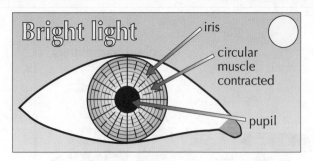

Bright light

iris

circular muscle contracted

pupil

1) <u>Very bright light</u> can <u>damage</u> the eye — so you have a reflex to protect it.

2) <u>Light receptors</u> in the eye detect very bright light and send a message along a <u>sensory neurone</u> to the brain.

3) The message then travels along a <u>relay neurone</u> to a <u>motor neurone</u>, which tells <u>circular muscles</u> in the <u>iris</u> (the coloured part of the eye) to <u>contract</u>, making the pupil smaller.

## Reflexes are faster than other responses

Reflexes <u>bypass</u> conscious parts of your brain completely when a super <u>quick</u> response is essential — your body just gets on with things. If you had to stop and think first, you'd end up a lot more sore (or worse).

# Warm-Up and Exam Questions

Welcome to some questions. There are quite a few of them, but that's because they're pretty important...

1) What is meant by the term 'stimulus'?
2) What is the function of an axon?
3) How does a myelin sheath speed up electrical impulses?
4) Name the three types of neurone in a reflex arc.
5) What name is given to the connection between two neurones?

## Exam Questions

1   A student is taking part in an experiment to test reaction times. Every time a red triangle appears on the computer screen in front of her, she has to click the mouse.

   (a)   Suggest what the stimulus, receptors and effectors are in this experiment.

   *[3 marks]*

   (b)   The student took the test three times. Her reaction time in test 1 was 328 ms.
         Her reaction time in test 2 was 346 ms. Her mean reaction time was 343 ms.
         Calculate her reaction time for test 3.

   *[2 marks]*

2   Young babies have several reflexes not usually present in adults. For example, if an object is placed in the palm of a newborn baby's hand, the baby will move their fingers to grasp the object. The reflex arc for this reflex is shown in **Figure 1**.

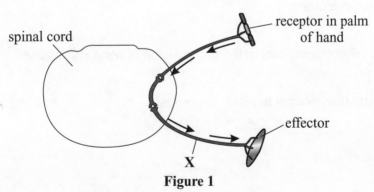

**Figure 1**

   (a)   Name the structure labelled **X** on **Figure 1**.

   *[1 mark]*

   (b)   State the type of effector in this response and describe its action.

   *[2 marks]*

   (c)   Explain how an electrical impulse in one neurone is able to pass to the next neurone.

   *[2 marks]*

   (d)   If an object is placed in the palm of a baby over 6 months old, it can choose whether it wants to
         grasp hold of the object. Describe **one** way in which the pathway of nervous impulses involved
         in grasping an object differs between a newborn baby and a baby older than 6 months.

   *[1 mark]*

# Revision Summary for Topic 2

Well, Topic 2 sure was a nerve-jangling topic — here's your chance to check you've learnt it.
Try these questions and tick off each one when you get it right.
When you've done all the questions under a heading and are completely happy, tick it off.

## Mitosis and Growth (p.37-40) ☑

1) What is the cell cycle? ☑
2) Give three uses of mitosis in organisms. ☑
3) Name the four stages of mitosis. Describe what happens in each one. ☑
4) Is the following statement true or false?
"The cells produced at the end of mitosis are identical to each other and the parent cell." ☑
5) Describe how animals grow. ☑
6) What major illness can result from uncontrolled cell division? ☑
7) Describe how a percentile chart is used to monitor growth. ☑

## Stem Cells (p.41-42) ☑

8) What is a stem cell? ☑
9) How are embryonic stem cells different to adult stem cells? ☑
10) What are meristems? Where are they found? ☑
11) What are the potential benefits of stem cells being used in medicine? ☑
12) Give three potential risks associated with using stem cells in medicine. ☑

## The Nervous System (p.44-46) ☑

13) What effect does a myelin sheath have on the speed of an electrical impulse? ☑
14) Draw and label a motor neurone. ☑
15) What is a synapse? ☑
16) Describe the role of neurotransmitters in the transmission of nervous impulses. ☑
17) What is a reflex arc? ☑
18) Why are reflexes faster than normal nervous responses? ☑

# Sexual Reproduction

If you've ever wondered why you look <u>like</u> your <u>family members</u>, but <u>not exactly the same</u>, read on...

## Sexual Reproduction Produces **Genetically Different Cells**

1) <u>Sexual reproduction</u> is where genetic information from <u>two</u> organisms (a <u>father</u> and a <u>mother</u>) is combined to produce offspring which are <u>genetically different</u> to either parent.

2) In <u>sexual reproduction</u>, the father and mother produce <u>gametes</u> (reproductive cells). In animals these are <u>sperm</u> and <u>egg cells</u>.

3) Gametes only contain <u>half the number</u> of <u>chromosomes</u> of normal cells — they are <u>haploid</u>. <u>Normal cells</u> (with the full number of chromosomes) are <u>diploid</u> (see p.37).

A human cell nucleus contains 46 chromosomes — so the diploid number for a human is 46 and the haploid number is 23.

4) At <u>fertilisation</u>, a male gamete <u>fuses</u> with a female gamete to produce a <u>fertilised egg</u>, also known as a <u>zygote</u>. The zygote ends up with the <u>full set</u> of chromosomes (so it is diploid).

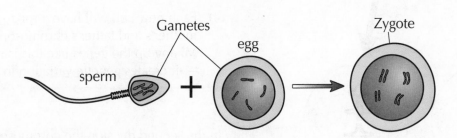

5) The zygote then undergoes <u>cell division</u> (by mitosis — see p.37-38) and develops into an <u>embryo</u>.

In flowering plants, the male gametes are found in the pollen and the female gametes are found in the ovaries at the bottom of the stigma.

6) The embryo <u>inherits characteristics</u> from <u>both parents</u>, as it has received a <u>mixture of chromosomes</u> (and therefore <u>genes</u>) from its mum and its dad.

## Sexual reproduction combines genetic information from two parents

Make sure you're confident with this page — it will make learning the next few pages much easier.

# Meiosis

This page is all about how gametes end up with <u>half</u> the number of <u>chromosomes</u> of a normal cell.

## Gametes are Produced by Meiosis

Meiosis is a type of <u>cell division</u>. It's different to mitosis because it <u>doesn't produce identical cells</u>. In humans, meiosis <u>only</u> happens in the <u>reproductive organs</u> (ovaries and testes).

This cell has duplicated each chromosome — each arm of the X-shape is identical.

chromosome pair

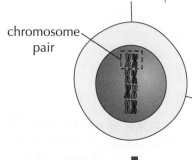

Half of the chromosomes in the starting cell were inherited from the organism's father (blue) and half from its mother (red).

DIVISION 1

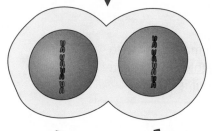

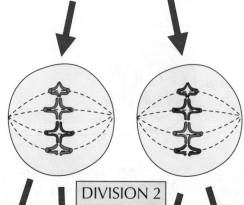

DIVISION 2

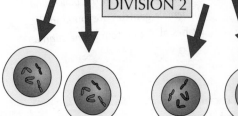

1) Before the cell starts to divide, it <u>duplicates</u> its <u>DNA</u> (so there's enough for each new cell). One arm of each X-shaped chromosome is an <u>exact copy</u> of the other arm.

2) In the <u>first division</u> in meiosis (there are two divisions) the chromosomes <u>line up</u> in pairs in the centre of the cell. One chromosome in each pair came from the organism's mother and one came from its father.

3) The <u>pairs</u> are then <u>pulled apart</u>, so each new cell only has one copy of each chromosome. <u>Some</u> of the father's chromosomes and <u>some</u> of the mother's chromosomes go into each new cell.

4) Each new cell will have a <u>mixture</u> of the mother's and father's chromosomes. Mixing up the genes like this is <u>really important</u> — it creates <u>genetic variation</u> in the offspring.

5) In the <u>second division</u> the chromosomes <u>line up</u> again in the centre of the cell. It's a lot like mitosis. The <u>arms</u> of the chromosomes are <u>pulled apart</u>.

6) You get <u>four haploid daughter cells</u> — these are the <u>gametes</u>. Each <u>gamete</u> only has a <u>single set</u> of chromosomes. The gametes are all <u>genetically different</u>.

## Meiosis is different from Mitosis

Don't get <u>meiosis</u> mixed up with <u>mitosis</u>. Try remembering m**it**osis has "IT" in it, "IT" for **I**dentical **T**wins, because the cells produced by mitosis are <u>genetically the same</u> — like identical twins. Meiosis doesn't have "IT" so it produces <u>daughter cells</u> which are <u>genetically different</u>.

# DNA

Reproduction is all about <u>passing on your DNA</u> to the next generation. This molecule carries all the <u>instructions</u> for your characteristics — so it's a big part of what makes you <u>you</u>.

## DNA is Made Up of Nucleotides

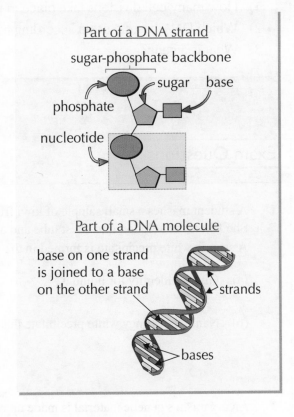

1) DNA strands are <u>polymers</u> made up of lots of repeating units called <u>nucleotides</u>.

2) Each nucleotide consists of <u>one sugar molecule</u>, <u>one phosphate molecule</u> and <u>one 'base'</u>.

3) The <u>sugar</u> and <u>phosphate</u> molecules in the nucleotides form a '<u>backbone</u>' to the DNA strands. The sugar and phosphate molecules <u>alternate</u>.

4) One of <u>four</u> different <u>bases</u> joins to each <u>sugar</u>. The bases are: <u>A</u> (adenine), <u>T</u> (thymine), <u>C</u> (cytosine) and <u>G</u> (guanine).

5) A DNA molecule has <u>two strands coiled together</u> in the shape of a <u>double helix</u> (a double stranded spiral).

6) Each base <u>links</u> to a base on the opposite strand in the helix.

7) A <u>always pairs</u> with T, and C <u>always pairs</u> with G. This is called <u>complementary base pairing</u>.

Complementary base pairs:

| A | T |
|---|---|
| C | G |

8) The complementary base pairs are joined together by <u>weak hydrogen bonds</u>.

## DNA is Stored as Chromosomes and Contains Genes

1) <u>Chromosomes</u> are <u>long</u>, <u>coiled up</u> molecules of <u>DNA</u>. They're found in the <u>nucleus</u> of <u>eukaryotic cells</u>.

2) A <u>gene</u> is a <u>section</u> of DNA on a chromosome that codes for a <u>particular protein</u>.

3) <u>All</u> of an organism's DNA makes up its <u>genome</u>.

## You Need to Know How to Extract DNA From Fruit Cells

Don't believe that cells contain DNA?
Well here's a <u>practical</u> you can do to get it out...

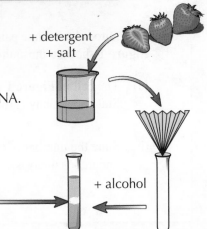

1) Mash some strawberries and then put them in a beaker containing a solution of <u>detergent</u> and <u>salt</u>. Mix well.
   - The <u>detergent</u> will <u>break down</u> the <u>cell membranes</u> to release the DNA.
   - The <u>salt</u> will make the <u>DNA stick together</u>.

2) <u>Filter</u> the mixture to get the <u>froth</u> and <u>big</u>, <u>insoluble</u> bits of cell out.

3) Gently add some <u>ice-cold alcohol</u> to the filtered mixture.

4) The DNA will start to come <u>out of solution</u> as it's <u>not soluble</u> in <u>cold alcohol</u>. It will appear as a <u>stringy white precipitate</u> (a solid) that can be carefully fished out with a <u>glass rod</u>.

# Warm-Up and Exam Questions

It's time to see how much you picked up about meiosis, reproduction and DNA.

## Warm-Up Questions

1) How many cell divisions take place in meiosis?
2) Which DNA bases pair up according to complementary base pairing?
3) What is a gene?

## Exam Questions

**1** A student mashes a small sample of kiwi fruit and then adds detergent and salt. She filters the solution into a test tube and adds liquid X. A stringy white precipitate is formed in the test tube.

*Grade 4-6*

(a) Give an identity for liquid X.

*[1 mark]*

(b) Name the stringy white precipitate that is formed.

*[1 mark]*

**2** An organism's genetic material is made up of a chemical called DNA.

*Grade 4-6*

(a) Which of the following describes the structure of DNA?

☐ **A** A protein made up of two strands.   ☐ **C** A polymer made up of two strands.

☐ **B** A protein made up of four strands.   ☐ **D** A polymer made up of four strands.

*[1 mark]*

(b) Name the type of bond that joins complementary base pairs.

*[1 mark]*

(c) Describe the relationship between DNA and the proteins produced by an organism.

*[3 marks]*

**3** Mosquitoes have three pairs of chromosomes in their body cells. **Figure 1** shows a mosquito cell which is about to divide by meiosis.

*Grade 6-7*

(a) The cell in **Figure 1** undergoes meiosis. State how many chromosomes will be present in each new cell produced.

*[1 mark]*

**Figure 1**

(b) State the number of cells that will be produced in total when the cell in **Figure 1** undergoes meiosis.

*[1 mark]*

# Genes and Alleles

Each pair of <u>chromosomes</u> contain the <u>same genes</u> in the <u>same places</u>. These genes can come in different <u>versions</u>, so the <u>characteristics</u> you have will depend on which versions you <u>inherit</u> from your parents.

## Alleles Are **Different Versions** of the **Same Gene**

1) What <u>genes</u> you <u>inherit</u> control what <u>characteristics</u> you <u>develop</u>.

2) <u>Different</u> genes control <u>different</u> characteristics. <u>Some</u> characteristics are controlled by a <u>single</u> gene. However, most characteristics are controlled by <u>several genes interacting</u>.

3) All genes exist in different <u>versions</u> called <u>alleles</u> (which are represented by <u>letters</u> in genetic diagrams).

4) You have <u>two</u> versions (alleles) of <u>every gene</u> in your body — <u>one</u> on <u>each chromosome</u> in a pair.

5) If an organism has <u>two alleles</u> for a particular gene that are <u>the same</u>, then it's <u>homozygous</u> for that trait. If its two alleles for a particular gene are <u>different</u>, then it's <u>heterozygous</u>.

6) Some alleles are <u>dominant</u> (shown with a <u>capital letter</u>, e.g. '<u>C</u>') and some are <u>recessive</u> (shown by a <u>small letter</u>, e.g. '<u>c</u>'). Dominant alleles <u>overrule</u> recessive alleles, so if an organism has <u>one dominant</u> and <u>one recessive</u> allele for a gene (e.g. '<u>Cc</u>'), then the <u>dominant allele</u> will determine what <u>characteristic</u> is present.

7) To display a <u>dominant characteristic</u>, an organism can have either <u>two dominant alleles</u> for a particular gene or <u>one dominant</u> and <u>one recessive</u> allele for that gene. But for an organism to display a <u>recessive</u> characteristic, <u>both</u> its alleles must be <u>recessive</u>.

8) Your <u>genotype</u> is the combination of <u>alleles</u> you have. Your alleles determine what characteristics you have — your <u>phenotype</u>. So <u>different</u> combinations of alleles give rise to <u>different</u> phenotypes.

## There are lots of fancy words to learn on this page...

Make sure you fully understand what all the <u>different terms</u> on this page mean (i.e. genes, alleles, homozygous, heterozygous, dominant, recessive, genotype and phenotype). You'll feel much more comfortable going into the exam knowing that these words aren't going to trip you up.

# Genetic Diagrams

## Genetic Diagrams Can Show Inheritance of a Single Characteristic

The inheritance of a <u>single</u> characteristic is called <u>monohybrid inheritance</u>.  You can use a <u>monohybrid cross</u> to show how <u>recessive</u> and <u>dominant</u> traits for a <u>single characteristic</u> are inherited.

For example, let's say an allele that causes hamsters to have superpowers is <u>recessive</u> ("b"), and that <u>normal</u> (boring) hamsters don't have superpowers due to a <u>dominant</u> allele ("B").  Here's how you could use a monohybrid cross to show the <u>probability</u> of either the <u>dominant</u> or <u>recessive</u> trait being <u>inherited</u>:

1) The first step is to cross two <u>homozygous</u> hamsters (BB and bb):    'Cross' just means 'breed together'.

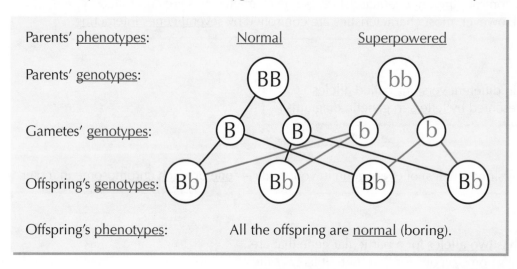

If a hamster has the genotype BB or Bb, its phenotype will be normal and boring.  If a hamster has the genotype bb, it will have superpowers.

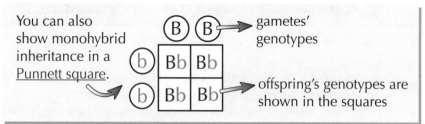

2) If two of these <u>offspring</u> now <u>breed</u>, you'll get the next generation:

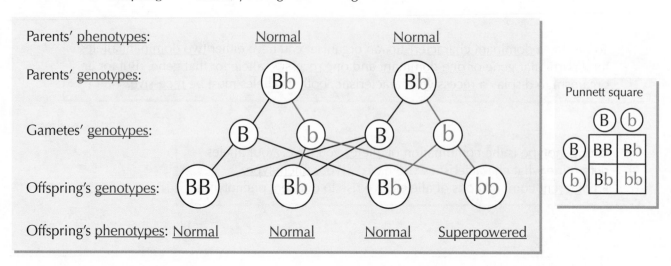

3) In this generation, there's a <u>3:1 ratio</u> of normal to superpowered offspring.  In other words, there's a <u>3 in 4</u> (<u>75%</u>) probability of <u>normal hamsters</u> and a <u>1 in 4</u> (<u>25%</u>) probability of <u>superpowers</u>.

# Genetic Diagrams

You can work out the <u>probability</u> of offspring being male or female by using a <u>genetic diagram</u>.

## A **Genetic Diagram** Can Show How **Sex** is **Determined** in **Humans**

1) There are <u>23 matched pairs</u> of chromosomes in every human body cell. The <u>23rd pair</u> is labelled <u>XX</u> or <u>XY</u>. They're the two chromosomes that decide whether you turn out <u>male</u> or <u>female</u>.

2) Males have an <u>X</u> and a <u>Y</u> chromosome (XY). The <u>Y</u> chromosome causes <u>male</u> characteristics.

3) Females have <u>two X chromosomes</u> (XX). The <u>XX combination</u> allows <u>female characteristics</u> to develop.

4) Because of this, there's an <u>equal chance</u> of having either a <u>boy</u> or a <u>girl</u>. Here's a <u>genetic diagram</u> to prove it:

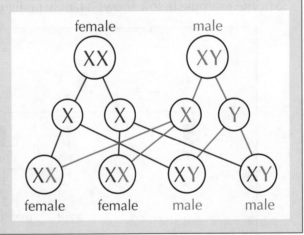

1) Even though we're talking about inheriting <u>chromosomes</u> here and not <u>single genes</u>, the <u>genetic diagram</u> still works the same way.

2) When you plug the letters into the diagram, it shows that there are <u>two XX</u> results and <u>two XY</u> results, so there's the <u>same probability</u> of getting a boy or a girl.

3) Don't forget that this <u>50 : 50 ratio</u> is <u>only a probability</u>. If you had four kids they could all be boys — or all girls.

5) All <u>eggs</u> have one <u>X chromosome</u>, but a <u>sperm</u> can have either an <u>X chromosome</u> or a <u>Y chromosome</u>. So <u>sex determination</u> in humans depends on whether the <u>sperm</u> that <u>fertilises</u> an egg carries an <u>X</u> or a <u>Y</u>.

## There are lots of diagrams on these pages...

There's a good chance you'll be asked to <u>draw</u> or <u>interpret</u> a genetic diagram or punnet square in the exam. Whether this is for sex determination, the inheritance of an allele you've looked at in class or one you've never heard of, the principle is <u>always the same</u> — so make sure you know how to use them.

# Genetic Diagrams

## Family Pedigrees Can Also Show Monohybrid Inheritance

Knowing how inheritance works helps you to interpret a family pedigree (a family tree of genetic disorders).
Here's an example using cystic fibrosis — a genetic disorder of the cell membranes.

### Cystic Fibrosis is a Recessive Genetic Disorder

1) The allele which causes cystic fibrosis (CF) is a recessive allele, 'f', carried by about 1 person in 30.

2) Because it's recessive, people with only one copy of the allele won't have the disorder
— they're known as carriers.

3) For a child to inherit the disorder, both parents must either have the disorder themselves or be carriers.

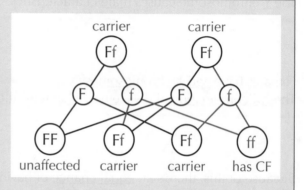

This diagram shows a monohybrid cross between two people who are carriers of the cystic fibrosis allele.

You can see from the diagram that there's a 1 in 4 chance of a child having the disorder if both parents are carriers.

The probability of each outcome can also be expressed as a ratio — 1 : 2 : 1 for unaffected : carrier : disorder.

4) You can show information about how alleles are passed through families on a family pedigree diagram.
The lines on the pedigree link the parents to each other (horizontal) and to their children (vertical).

5) The example below shows a family pedigree for a family that includes carriers of cystic fibrosis:

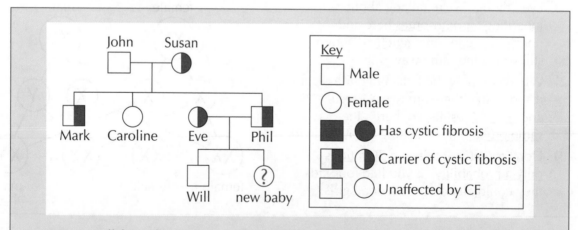

- You can tell from the pedigree that the allele for cystic fibrosis isn't dominant because plenty of family members carry the allele but don't have the disorder.

- There is a 1 in 4 (25%) chance that the new baby will have cystic fibrosis and a 1 in 2 (50%) chance that it will be a carrier (because both of its parents are carriers).

- In fact, the case of the new baby is the same as in the monohybrid cross diagram above — they could be unaffected (FF), be a carrier (Ff) or have the disorder (ff).

## It's enough to make you go cross-eyed...

If you're struggling to interpret a family pedigree in the exam, try writing the genotype of each person on to it. You might get a family tree showing the inheritance of a dominant allele instead — in this case, there won't be any carriers (because everyone with the allele has that phenotype).

# Warm-Up and Exam Questions

Take a deep breath and go through these Warm-Up Questions one by one. Then on to the
Exam Questions. Don't panic if you get something wrong — as they say, practice makes perfect...

## Warm-Up Questions

1) What are alleles?

2) What does phenotype mean?

3) For a certain type of mouse, having the genotype bb results in white fur. Having the genotype
   Bb or BB, results in brown fur. Which characteristic, white fur or brown fur is recessive?
   Explain your answer.

4) What combination of sex chromosomes do human females have?

## Exam Questions

1   Cystic fibrosis is a genetic disorder caused by a recessive allele.

    **F** = normal allele   **f** = faulty allele that leads to cystic fibrosis

    **Figure 1** is an incomplete Punnett square showing the
    possible inheritance of cystic fibrosis from one couple.

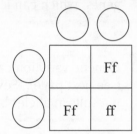

**Figure 1**

   (a)   Complete the Punnett square to show the genotype of
         the missing offspring and the genotypes of the gametes.

                                                                    *[2 marks]*

   (b)   Give the proportion of the possible offspring that are homozygous.

                                                                    *[1 mark]*

   (c)   State the phenotype of the possible offspring with the genotype ff.

                                                                    *[1 mark]*


2   Albinism is a condition characterised by the lack of pigment in the hair and skin.
    It is caused by the recessive allele **a**. The dominant allele **A** results in normal pigmentation.

   (a)   State the possible genotypes of a rabbit that shows no symptoms of albinism.

                                                                    *[1 mark]*

    A rabbit with albinism mated with a rabbit that showed no symptoms of the condition.
    56% of the offspring had albinism.

   (b)   Deduce the genotypes of the parent rabbits and the possible genotypes of their offspring.
         Use a genetic diagram to explain your answer.

                                                                    *[3 marks]*

   (c)   Using your genetic diagram, give the percentage of offspring that are likely to have albinism.

                                                                    *[1 mark]*

   (d)   Suggest why the percentage of offspring which were born with albinism
         was not exactly the same as that suggested by your genetic diagram.

                                                                    *[1 mark]*

# Variation

You'll probably have noticed that not all people are identical.  There are reasons for this.

## Organisms of the **Same Species** Have **Differences**

1) Different species look different.

2) But even organisms of the same species will usually look at least slightly different.
   E.g. all dogs are the same species, but a Dalmatian looks quite different to a Pug.

3) These differences are called the variation within a species.  It can be genetic or environmental.

4) Genetic variation within a species is caused by organisms having different alleles (versions of genes) which can lead to differences in phenotype (the characteristics an organism displays).

5) Genetic variation can be caused by new alleles arising through mutations (see next page).  Sexual reproduction also causes genetic variation since it results in alleles being combined in lots of different ways in offspring.

*Sexual reproduction means no two members of a species are genetically identical (apart from identical twins).*

6) There tends to be a lot of genetic variation within a population of a species.
   This is mostly due to neutral mutations (see next page).

7) Variation within a species can also be caused by the environment (the conditions in which organisms live).  For example:

 A plant grown on a nice sunny windowsill could grow luscious and green.    The same plant grown in darkness would grow tall and spindly and its leaves would turn yellow.

These environmental variations in phenotype are also known as acquired characteristics.
They're characteristics that organisms acquire (get) during their lifetimes.

8) Most variation in phenotype is determined by a mixture of genetic and environmental factors.

For example, the maximum height that an animal or plant could grow to is determined by its genes.
But whether it actually grows that tall depends on its environment (e.g. how much food it gets).

## You can't blame all of your faults on your parents...

Although the genes that you inherit from your parents are really important at determining what characteristics you have, the conditions in which you live usually play a role too.

# Variation and the Human Genome Project

## Alleles Arise Due to Genetic Mutations

1) Mutations are changes to the base sequence of DNA.

2) When they occur within a gene they result in an allele, or a different version of the gene.

3) They don't always have a big effect on the phenotype of an organism.
   In fact, most mutations don't have any effect — in other words they are neutral.

4) But some mutations do have a small effect on the phenotype —
   they alter an individual's characteristics, but only very slightly.
   E.g. a mutation might give a hamster long hair instead of short hair.

5) Very rarely, a single mutation will have a big effect on phenotype.  For example, it might result
   in the production of a protein that is so different that it can no longer carry out its function.

This is what happens in cystic fibrosis (see page 56).  A mutation causes a protein
that controls the movement of salt and water into and out of cells to stop working
properly.  This leads to the production of thick, sticky mucus in the lungs and the
digestive system, which can make it difficult to breathe and digest food.

6) New combinations of alleles may also interact with each other to produce new phenotypes.

## Over 20 000 Genes Were Mapped in the Human Genome Project

1) Thousands of scientists from all over the world collaborated (worked together) on
   the Human Genome Project.  The big idea was to find every single human gene.

2) The project officially started in 1990 and a complete map of the human genome,
   including the locations of around 20 500 genes, was completed in 2003.

3) Now that the genes have all been found, scientists are trying to figure out what they all do.

4) So far, the project has helped to identify about 1800 genes related to disease,
   which has huge potential benefits for medicine (see next page).

# The Human Genome Project

Here's a bit more about the Human Genome Project — including how we might use the data it produced.

## There are Lots of Medical Applications for the Project's Research

### Prediction and prevention of diseases

Many common diseases like cancers and heart disease are caused by the interaction of different genes, as well as lifestyle factors. If doctors knew what genes predisposed people to what diseases, we could all get individually tailored advice on the best diet and lifestyle to avoid our likely problems. Doctors could also check us regularly to ensure early treatment if we do develop the diseases we're susceptible to.

### Testing and treatment for inherited disorders

1) Inherited disorders (e.g. cystic fibrosis) are caused by the presence of one or more faulty alleles in a person's genome.

2) Thanks to the Human Genome Project, scientists are now able to identify the genes and alleles that are suspected of causing an inherited disorder much more quickly than they could do in the past.

3) Once an allele that causes an inherited disorder has been identified, people can be tested for it and it may be possible to develop better treatments or even (eventually) a cure for the disease.

### New and better medicines

1) Genome research has highlighted some common genetic variations between people. Some variations affect how our individual bodies will react to certain diseases and to the possible treatments for them.

2) Scientists can use this knowledge to design new drugs that are specifically tailored to people with a particular genetic variation. They can also determine how well an existing drug will work for an individual. Tests can already identify whether or not someone with breast cancer will respond to a particular drug, and what dosage is most appropriate for certain drugs in different patients.

3) More generally, knowing how a disease affects us on a molecular level should make it possible to design more effective treatments with fewer side-effects.

## But There Could Also be Drawbacks

1) Increased stress — for example, if someone knew from an early age that they're susceptible to a nasty brain disease, they could panic every time they get a headache (even if they never get the disease).

2) Gene-ism — people with genetic problems could come under pressure not to have children.

3) Discrimination by employers and insurers — life insurance could become impossible to get (or expensive at least) if you have any genetic likelihood of serious disease. And employers might discriminate against people who are genetically likely to get a disease.

## Scientists can learn a lot about diseases from the human genome

Working out the human genome was a massive project — it involved scientists from many different parts of the world and took more than ten years to complete. Still, if scientists can use the information to help us understand more about diseases and how to fight them, then I reckon it was well worth all the effort.

# Warm-Up and Exam Questions

By doing these questions, you'll soon find out if you've got the basic facts straight.

## Warm-Up Questions

1) Explain what is meant by environmental variation.
2) Amy and Beth are sisters. Amy's hair is curly and Beth's hair is straight. Suggest one way that this difference could be caused by a) a genetic factor, b) an environmental factor.
3) True or False? Genetic mutations in an organism's DNA always have an effect on the organism's phenotype.

## Exam Questions

1 Helen and Stephanie are identical twins. This means they have identical DNA. *(Grade 4-6)*

(a) Which of the following characteristics can you be certain that Helen and Stephanie will share?

- A They will speak the same language.
- B They will be the same height.
- C They will both be fast runners.
- D They will have the same blood group.

*[1 mark]*

(b) Helen weighs 7 kg more than Stephanie.
Explain whether this is due to genes, environmental factors or both.

*[2 marks]*

(c) Stephanie has a birthmark on her shoulder. Helen doesn't.
State whether this type of birthmark is caused by genes and explain your answer.

*[1 mark]*

2 A group of scientists used data from the Human Genome Project to identify an allele that puts people who carry it at high risk of developing colorectal cancer. Eshan has a family history of colorectal cancer. He is offered a genetic test that will tell him if he is carries the allele or not. *(Grade 6-7)*

(a) Suggest **one** advantage to Eshan of having this genetic test.

*[1 marks]*

(b) Suggest **one** disadvantage to Eshan of having this genetic test.

*[1 mark]*

3 Genetic variation in a population arises partly due to mutations. *(Grade 6-7)*

(a) Explain how mutations can increase variation in a species.

*[3 marks]*

(b) Some mutations are neutral, having no effect on an organism, but some do have an impact.
Suggest how a single mutation could have a large impact on phenotype.

*[2 marks]*

# Revision Summary for Topic 3

That's <u>Topic 3</u> done with — make sure you can answer these questions before moving on.
Try these questions and <u>tick off each one</u> when you <u>get it right</u>.
When you've done <u>all the questions</u> under a heading and are <u>completely happy</u> with it, tick it off..

## Reproduction and Meiosis (p.49-50) ☑

1) Name the gametes in humans. ☑

2) What happens to the DNA in a cell before the first division in meiosis? ☑

## DNA (p.51) ☑

3) What are the repeating units that make up DNA? ☑

4) What is meant by the term 'double helix'? ☑

5) When extracting DNA from a fruit, what is the purpose of mixing the fruit with detergent? ☑

6) What effect does ice-cold alcohol have on a solution containing free DNA molecules? ☑

## Genes, Alleles and Genetic Diagrams (p.53-56) ☑  ☑

7) What does it mean if an organism is
   a) homozygous for a gene?
   b) heterozygous for a gene? ☑

8) What is monohybrid inheritance? ☑

9) A couple have a child.
   What's the probability that the child will have the XX combination of sex chromosomes? ☑

10) How are carriers shown on a family pedigree? ☑

## Variation and The Human Genome Project (p.58-60) ☑

11) What causes genetic variation in a species? ☑

12) What is an acquired characteristic? ☑

13) Write down three applications of the knowledge gained from the Human Genome Project. ☑

14) Describe three potential drawbacks of being able to read a person's genome. ☑

# Natural Selection and Evidence for Evolution

Evolution is the <u>slow and continuous change</u> of organisms from one generation to the next. <u>Charles Darwin</u> came up with the theory of <u>natural selection</u> to explain how <u>evolution</u> occurs.

## Natural Selection Means "Survival of the Fittest"

1) Individuals in a population show <u>genetic variation</u> because of differences in their <u>alleles</u> (see page 58). New alleles arise through <u>mutations</u>.

*Alleles are versions of genes — see page 53.*

2) Things like <u>predation</u>, <u>competition</u> for resources (e.g. food, water, mates, etc.) and <u>disease</u> act as <u>selection pressures</u>. This means they affect an organism's chance of <u>surviving</u> and <u>reproducing</u>.

3) Those individuals with <u>characteristics</u> that make them <u>better adapted</u> to the selection pressures in their environment have a <u>better chance of survival</u> and so are more likely to <u>breed</u> successfully.

4) This means the <u>alleles</u> that are responsible for the useful characteristics are more likely to be <u>passed on</u> to the <u>next generation</u>.

5) However, some individuals will be <u>less well adapted</u> to the selection pressures in their environment and may be less able to <u>compete</u>. These individuals are <u>less likely</u> to survive and reproduce.

*A species that can't compete is likely to go extinct.*

6) The <u>beneficial characteristics</u> become more <u>common</u> in the population over time.

## Fossils Provide Evidence for Evolution

1) A fossil is <u>any trace</u> of an animal or plant that lived <u>a long time ago</u> (e.g. over a thousand years). They are most commonly found in <u>rocks</u>. Generally, the <u>deeper</u> the rock, the <u>older</u> the fossil.

2) By arranging fossils in <u>chronological</u> (date) order, <u>gradual changes</u> in organisms can be observed. This provides <u>evidence</u> for evolution, because it shows how species have <u>changed</u> and <u>developed</u> over billions of years. Fossils that provide evidence for <u>human evolution</u> are covered on page 65.

---

## Natural selection — the fittest pass on their alleles...

Natural selection's all about the organisms with the <u>best characteristics</u> surviving to <u>pass on</u> their <u>alleles</u>, so that the whole species ends up adapted to its environment. It doesn't happen overnight though.

# Natural Selection and Evidence for Evolution

It's not just fossils from many, many years ago that provide <u>evidence for evolution</u> — we can observe the process of <u>natural selection</u> happening in real-time in <u>bacteria</u>...

## Bacteria Provide Evidence for Evolution

1) Like all organisms, bacteria sometimes develop <u>random mutations</u> in their DNA. These can create <u>new alleles</u>, which can <u>change</u> the bacteria's <u>characteristics</u> — e.g. a bacterium could become <u>less affected</u> by a particular <u>antibiotic</u> (a drug designed to kill bacteria or prevent them from reproducing).

2) For the bacterium, the ability to <u>resist</u> this antibiotic is a big <u>advantage</u>. In a host who's being treated to get rid of the infection, a resistant bacterium is <u>better able to survive</u> than a non-resistant bacterium — and so it lives for longer and <u>reproduces</u> many more times.

3) This leads to the allele for antibiotic resistance being <u>passed on</u> to lots of offspring — it's just <u>natural selection</u>. This is how it spreads and becomes <u>more common</u> in a population of bacteria over time.

*It's easy to see evolution happening in bacteria because they reproduce so rapidly.*

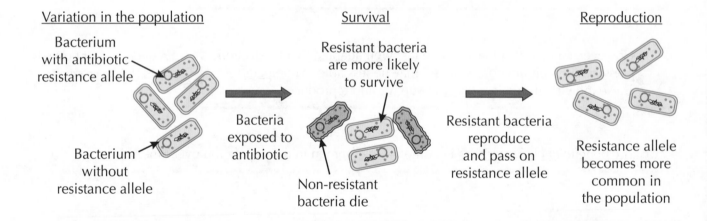

Variation in the population

Bacterium with antibiotic resistance allele

Bacterium without resistance allele

Bacteria exposed to antibiotic

Survival

Resistant bacteria are more likely to survive

Non-resistant bacteria die

Resistant bacteria reproduce and pass on resistance allele

Reproduction

Resistance allele becomes more common in the population

4) Antibiotic resistance provides <u>evidence</u> for evolution because it makes the bacteria <u>better adapted</u> to an <u>environment</u> in which <u>antibiotics</u> (a <u>selection pressure</u>) are <u>present</u>. And as a result, antibiotic resistance becomes <u>more common</u> in the population over time.

5) The emergence of <u>other</u> resistant organisms (e.g. <u>rats</u> resistant to the poison <u>warfarin</u>) <u>also</u> provides evidence for evolution.

## Don't become resistant to revision...

Evolution by natural selection is a <u>theory</u> — an <u>accepted hypothesis</u>. <u>Evidence</u> is really important when it comes to accepting or rejecting scientific hypotheses — if there's no evidence to support a hypothesis, it won't become a theory.

# Evidence for Human Evolution

There's a lot of <u>fossil evidence</u> that suggests that humans evolved from a <u>common ancestor</u> with other <u>apes</u>.

## Fossils Give Us Clues About **What Human Ancestors** Were Like

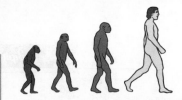

1) Evidence from <u>fossils</u> suggests that humans and chimpanzees evolved from a <u>common ancestor</u> that existed around 6 million years ago.

2) Human beings and their ancestors are known as <u>hominids</u>. Fossils of several different <u>hominid species</u> have been found.

3) These fossils have characteristics that are <u>between</u> apes and humans — by looking at <u>hominid fossils</u> you can see how humans have <u>evolved</u> over time.

## 'Ardi' is a Fossil Hominid **4.4 Million Years Old**

<u>Ardi</u> is a <u>fossil</u> of the species *Ardipithecus ramidus*. She was found in Ethiopia and is <u>4.4 million years old</u>. Ardi's features are a <u>mixture</u> of those found in humans and in apes:

1) The structure of her <u>feet</u> suggests she <u>climbed trees</u> — she had an <u>ape-like big toe</u> to grasp branches.

2) She also had <u>long arms</u> and <u>short legs</u> (more like an ape than a human).

3) Her <u>brain size</u> was about the same as a <u>chimpanzee's</u>.

4) But the structure of her legs suggests that she <u>walked upright</u>. Her <u>hand bone</u> structure also suggests she didn't use her <u>hands</u> to help her <u>walk</u> (like <u>apes</u> do).

Brain size is found by working out 'cranial capacity' — the space taken up by the brain in the skull.

## 'Lucy' is a Fossil Hominid **3.2 Million Years Old**

<u>Lucy</u> is a fossil of the species *Australopithecus afarensis*. She was found in Ethiopia and is <u>3.2 million years old</u>. Lucy also has a <u>mixture</u> of human and ape features, but she is <u>more human-like</u> than Ardi.

1) Lucy had <u>arched feet</u>, more adapted to walking than climbing, and no ape-like big toe.

2) The size of her <u>arms</u> and <u>legs</u> was <u>between</u> what you would expect to find in apes and humans.

3) Her <u>brain</u> was <u>slightly larger</u> than Ardi's but still similar in size to a <u>chimp's brain</u>.

4) The structure of Lucy's leg bones and feet suggest she <u>walked upright</u>, but more <u>efficiently</u> than Ardi.

## Leakey and His Team Found **Fossil Hominids 1.6 Million Years Old**

In 1984 scientist <u>Richard Leakey</u> organised an expedition to Kenya to look for <u>hominid fossils</u>. He and his team discovered <u>many important fossils</u> of different *Australopithecus* and *Homo* species.

1) One find was <u>Turkana Boy</u> — a <u>1.6 million year old</u> fossil skeleton of the species *Homo erectus*. He has a <u>mixture</u> of human and ape-like features, but is <u>more human-like</u> than Lucy.

2) His <u>short arms</u> and <u>long legs</u> are much more like a <u>human</u> than an <u>ape</u>, and his <u>brain size</u> was <u>much larger</u> than Lucy's — similar to <u>human</u> brain size.

3) The structure of his legs and feet suggest he was even better adapted to <u>walking upright</u> than Lucy.

# Evidence for Human Evolution

## You Can Show Human Evolution on a Timeline

So you know that the _Ardipithecus_ and _Australopithecus_ species were more ape-like, compared to the _Homo_ species, which are human-like. They can all be put on a timeline, showing how humans have evolved:

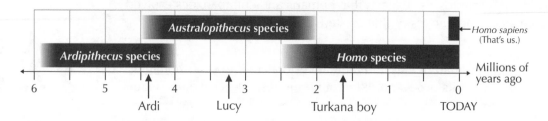

## Stone Tools Provide More Evidence for Human Evolution

The different _Homo_ species continued to evolve. You can tell this because they started using stone tools and these gradually became more complex (so their brains must have been getting larger):

| Homo species | Tool use | |
|---|---|---|
| Homo habilis (2.5-1.5 million years ago) | Made simple stone tools called pebble tools by hitting rocks together to make sharp flakes. These could be used to scrape meat from bones or crack bones open. |  |
| Homo erectus (2-0.3 million years ago) | Sculpted rocks into shapes to produce more complex tools like simple hand-axes. These could be used to hunt, dig, chop and scrape meat from bones. | |
| Homo neanderthalensis (300 000-25 000 years ago) | More complex tools. Evidence of flint tools, pointed tools and wooden spears. | |
| Homo sapiens (200 000 years ago-present) | Flint tools widely used. Pointed tools including arrowheads, fish hooks and needles appeared around 50 000 years ago. | |

## Stone Tools and Fossils Can be Dated

When an ancient stone tool or hominid fossil (see previous page) is found, there are several different ways scientists can work out how old it is. These include:

_Dating tools and fossils isn't always very accurate, e.g. rock layers can move over time._

1) Looking at the structural features of the tool or fossil. For example, simpler tools are likely to be older than more complex tools.

2) Using stratigraphy — the study of rock layers. Older rock layers are normally found below younger layers, so tools or fossils in deeper layers are usually older.

3) Stone tools are sometimes found with carbon-containing material, for instance a wooden handle. Carbon-14 dating can be used to date this material.

## Don't get bogged down by all this information...

It's a bit mind-boggling really how fossils can still exist even millions of years after the organism died. They really are fascinating things, and scientists have learned a whole lot from studying them in detail.

# Classification

It seems to be a basic human urge to want to <u>classify</u> things — that's the case in biology anyway...

## Classification is Organising **Living Organisms** into Groups

1) Traditionally, organisms were <u>classified</u> according to similarities and differences in their <u>observable characteristics</u>, i.e. things you can see (like how many legs something has). As <u>technology improved</u>, this included things you can see with a <u>microscope</u>, e.g. <u>cell structure</u>.

2) These characteristics were used to classify organisms in the <u>five kingdom classification system</u>. In this system, living things are first divided into <u>five groups</u> called <u>kingdoms</u>. These are:

- <u>Animals</u> — fish, mammals, reptiles, etc.
- <u>Plants</u> — grasses, trees, etc.
- <u>Fungi</u> — mushrooms and toadstools, yeasts, mould.
- <u>Prokaryotes</u> — all <u>single-celled</u> organisms <u>without</u> a nucleus.
- <u>Protists</u> — <u>eukaryotic single-celled</u> organisms, e.g. algae.

There's more on prokaryotes and eukaryotes on p.17.

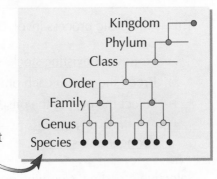

3) The <u>kingdoms</u> are then subdivided into smaller and smaller groups that have common features — <u>phylum</u>, <u>class</u>, <u>order</u>, <u>family</u>, <u>genus</u>, <u>species</u>.

## Classification Systems Change Over Time

1) The <u>five kingdom</u> classification system is still used, but it's now a bit <u>out of date</u>.

2) Over time, <u>technology</u> has developed further and our understanding of things like <u>biochemical processes</u> and <u>genetics</u> has increased. For example, we are now able to determine the <u>sequence of DNA bases</u> in different organisms' <u>genes</u> and <u>compare them</u> — the more <u>similar</u> the sequence of a gene, the more <u>closely related</u> the organisms.

There's more on DNA on page 51.

3) This led to a bit of a rethink about the way organisms are <u>classified</u> and to the proposal of the <u>three domain system</u> of classification by a scientist called Carl Woese.

4) Using <u>genetic analysis</u>, Woese found that some members of the <u>Prokaryote kingdom</u> were not as closely related as first thought. He proposed that this kingdom should be split into two groups called <u>Archaea</u> and <u>Bacteria</u>.

5) In fact, Woese suggested that all organisms should first be divided into <u>three large groups</u> called <u>domains</u>. Archaea and Bacteria are <u>two</u> of these domains, and the third domain is <u>Eukarya</u>.

ARCHAEA — Organisms in this domain <u>look similar</u> to <u>bacteria</u> but are actually quite <u>different</u> — as differences in their <u>genetic sequences</u> show. They were first found in <u>extreme places</u> such as hot springs and salt lakes.

BACTERIA — This domain contains <u>true bacteria</u> like *E. coli* and *Staphylococcus*.

EUKARYA — This domain includes a <u>broad range</u> of organisms including <u>fungi</u>, <u>plants</u>, <u>animals</u> and <u>protists</u>.

6) The three domains are then <u>subdivided</u> into <u>smaller groups</u> used in the <u>five kingdom system</u> (beginning with kingdom and finishing with species).

# Selective Breeding

'Selective breeding' sounds like it has the potential to be a tricky topic, but it's not too bad really.
You just take the best plants or animals and breed them together to get the best possible offspring. That's it.

## Selective Breeding is Very Simple

Selective breeding is when humans artificially select the plants or animals that are going
to breed so that the genes for particular characteristics remain in the population.
Organisms are selectively bred to develop features that are useful or attractive. For example:

- Animals that produce more meat or milk.
- Crops with disease resistance.
- Dogs with a good, gentle temperament.
- Plants that produce bigger fruit.

This is the basic process involved in selective breeding:

1) From your existing stock, select the ones which have the characteristics you're after.
2) Breed them with each other.
3) Select the best of the offspring, and breed them together.
4) Continue this process over several generations, and the desirable trait gets
   stronger and stronger. Eventually, all the offspring will have the characteristic.

Selective breeding
is also known as
'artificial selection'.

Selective breeding is nothing new — people have been doing it for thousands of years. It's how we
ended up with edible crops from wild plants and how we got domesticated animals like cows and dogs.

## Selective Breeding is Useful...

Selective breeding is important in agriculture and medical research. For example:

### In agriculture

Genetic variation means some cattle will have
better characteristics for producing meat than
others (e.g. a larger size). To improve meat
yields, a farmer could select cows and bulls with
these characteristics and breed them together.
After doing this, and selecting the best of the
offspring for several generations, the farmer
would get cows with a very high meat yield.

### In medical research

In several studies investigating the reasons
behind alcoholism, rats have been bred with
either a strong preference for alcohol or a
weak preference for alcohol.
This has allowed researchers to compare the
differences between the two different types of
rats, including differences in their behaviour
and in the way that their brains work.

## ...but Also Has Disadvantages

1) The main problem with selective breeding is that it reduces the gene pool — the number of
   different alleles (forms of a gene) in a population. This is because the "best" animals or plants
   are always used for breeding — and they are all closely related. This is known as inbreeding.

2) Inbreeding can cause health problems because there's more chance of the organisms inheriting harmful
   genetic defects when the gene pool is limited. Some dog breeds are susceptible to certain defects
   because of inbreeding, e.g. pugs often have breathing problems. This leads to ethical considerations —
   particularly if animals are deliberately bred to have negative characteristics for medical research.

3) There can also be serious problems if a new disease appears. There's not much variation in the
   population, so there's less chance of resistance alleles being present. All the stock are closely related to
   each other, so if one is going to be killed by a new disease, the others are also likely to succumb to it.

# Genetic Engineering

Genetic engineering is a relatively new area of science (well, it began in the 1970s). We've already put the technology to good use and it has many more exciting possibilities too...

## Genetic Engineering is Useful in **Agriculture** and **Medicine**

Genetic engineering involves modifying an organism's genome (its DNA) to introduce desirable characteristics.  For example:

In agriculture, crops can be genetically modified to be resistant to herbicides (chemicals that kill plants).  Making crops herbicide-resistant means farmers can spray their crops to kill weeds, without affecting the crop itself.  This can also increase crop yield.

In medicine, bacteria can be genetically engineered to produce human insulin, (see next page).

Researchers have managed to transfer human genes that produce useful proteins into sheep and cows.  E.g. human antibodies used in therapy for illnesses like arthritis, some types of cancer and multiple sclerosis. These proteins can then be extracted from the animal, e.g. from their milk.

It's possible that animals with organs suitable for organ transplantation into humans might also be produced in the future.

## Genetic Engineering Comes With **Risks**

1) Genetic engineering has risks as well as benefits.

2) There are concerns about growing genetically modified crops.  One is that transplanted genes may get out into the environment.  E.g. a herbicide resistance gene may be picked up by weeds, creating a new 'superweed' variety.  Another concern is that genetically modified crops could adversely affect food chains — or even human health.

3) There are also concerns about the genetic engineering of animals.  It can be hard to predict what effect modifying its genome will have on the organism — many genetically modified embryos don't survive and some genetically modified animals suffer from health problems later in life.

## Genetic engineering has huge potential benefits...

Scientists have used genetic engineering to produce organisms that benefit humans in all sorts of ways — from bacteria that can make medicines for us, to food crops that contain extra vitamins. But, as with any new technology, we need to be aware of the risks that it carries too.

# Genetic Engineering

The process of <u>transferring</u> a <u>new gene</u> into another <u>organism's</u> genome requires <u>enzymes</u> and <u>vectors</u>.

## Enzymes Can Cut Up DNA or Join DNA Pieces Together

1) <u>Restriction enzymes</u> recognise <u>specific sequences</u> of DNA and <u>cut the DNA</u> at these points — the pieces of DNA are left with <u>sticky ends</u> where they have been cut.
2) <u>Ligase</u> enzymes are used to join <u>two pieces of DNA</u> together at their <u>sticky ends</u>.
3) <u>Two different</u> bits of DNA stuck together are known as <u>recombinant DNA</u>.

## Vectors Can Be Used To Insert DNA Into Other Organisms

A vector is something that's used to transfer DNA into a cell. There are two sorts — <u>plasmids</u> and <u>viruses</u>:

1) Plasmids are <u>small</u>, <u>circular</u> molecules of DNA that can be <u>transferred</u> between <u>bacteria</u>.
2) Viruses <u>insert</u> DNA into the organisms they <u>infect</u>.

Here's how genetic engineering works:

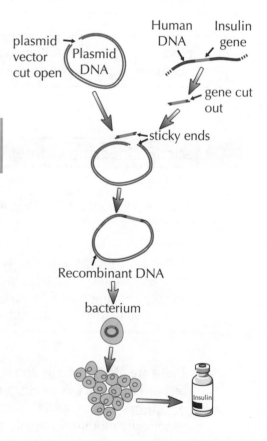

1) The <u>DNA</u> you want to <u>insert</u> (e.g. the gene for human insulin) is cut out with a <u>restriction enzyme</u>. The <u>vector DNA</u> is then cut open using the <u>same</u> restriction enzyme.

2) The vector DNA and the DNA you're inserting are left with <u>sticky ends</u>. They are <u>mixed together</u> with <u>ligase enzymes</u>.

3) The ligases <u>join</u> the pieces of DNA together to make <u>recombinant DNA</u>.

4) The recombinant DNA (i.e. the vector containing new DNA) is <u>inserted</u> into other cells, e.g. bacteria.

5) These cells can now <u>use the gene you inserted</u> to <u>make the protein</u> you want. E.g. <u>bacteria</u> containing the gene for <u>human insulin</u> can be grown in huge numbers in a fermenter to produce <u>insulin</u> for people with <u>diabetes</u>.

---

## It looks hard, but it's a fancy cut and paste...

The process of genetic engineering uses <u>two</u> key types of <u>enzyme</u>. Make sure you know the names of both types of enzyme for the exam and what they're used for in genetic engineering.

# Warm-Up and Exam Questions

There's only one way to do well in the exam — learn the facts and practise, practise, practise. We couldn't have made it much easier for you — so have a go.

## Warm-Up Questions

1) Why is a beneficial characteristic likely to become more common in a population over time?
2) What is a fossil?
3) Give one example of how advances in technology allowed scientists to distinguish between Archaea and Bacteria.
4) Name two types of enzyme needed for the process of genetic engineering.

## Exam Questions

1   Most populations of organisms show a lot of variation due to differences in their alleles.

(a)   State how new alleles arise in a population.

*[1 mark]*

A selection pressure is a change in an environment which can affect the chance of an organism surviving and reproducing.

(b)   (i)  Give **two** examples of a selection pressure in an environment.

*[2 marks]*

(ii) Explain why some organisms may not be able to survive if a new selection pressure is introduced to the environment.

*[2 marks]*

2   The characteristics of two varieties of wheat plants are shown in **Figure 1**.

| Variety | Grain yield | Resistance to bad weather |
|---|---|---|
| Tall stems | High | Low |
| Dwarf stems | Low | High |

**Figure 1**

(a)   Describe how selective breeding could be used to create a wheat plant with a high grain yield and high resistance to bad weather.

*[3 marks]*

(b)   Explain why selectively breeding the wheat plants could cause problems if the selectively bred wheat plants are exposed to a new wheat disease.

*[3 marks]*

# Exam Questions

**3** Scientists can carry out genetic analysis of DNA to determine the evolutionary relationships between organisms.

Figure 2 shows the percentage similarities between the DNA sequences of humans and four other organisms.

| Organism | A | B | C | D |
|---|---|---|---|---|
| % DNA sequence similarity to humans | 18 | 44 | 92 | 54 |

**Figure 2**

(a) Suggest which of the organisms, A-D, is most closely related to humans. Explain your answer.

*[2 marks]*

(b) Genetic analysis led the scientist Carl Woese to propose the three domain classification system. Name the three domains in this system.

*[3 marks]*

**4** *Clostridium difficile* is a bacterium that causes diarrhoea when it infects the bowel.

Infections by *Clostridium difficile* are becoming increasingly difficult to treat as some strains of the bacterium have developed resistance to a number of antibiotics.

Explain how a population of *Clostridium difficile* bacteria could have developed resistance to an antibiotic.

*[4 marks]*

**5\*** Figure 3 shows a type of stingray. The stingray's appearance mimics a flat rock. It spends most of its time on a rocky sea bed.

**Figure 3**

Explain how the stingray might have evolved to look like this.

*[6 marks]*

# Revision Summary for Topic 4

Well, it's all over for Topic 4 folks — but I know how much you'll miss it, so here are some questions on it...
Try these questions and tick off each one when you get it right.
When you've done all the questions under a heading and are completely happy, tick it off.

## Natural Selection and Evolution (p.63-66) ☑

1) Describe how organisms evolve by the process of natural selection. ☑
2) How do antibiotic-resistant bacteria provide evidence for evolution? ☑
3) What are hominids? ☑
4) Which fossil is older — "Ardi" or "Lucy"? ☑
5) Who was Richard Leakey? What important discoveries
   did he make in relation to human evolution? ☑
6) What is stratigraphy? How might it be used to date stone tools? ☑

## Classification (p.67) ☑

7) Describe how organisms were classified using the five kingdom classification system. ☑
8) What classification system was proposed by Carl Woese and what led him to propose it? ☑

## Selective Breeding (p.68) ☑

9) What is artificial selection? ☑
10) How can selective breeding be used to improve yields in the meat industry? ☑
11) Describe one way in which selective breeding can be useful outside of agriculture. ☑
12) What is a gene pool? ☑
13) Why does selective breeding reduce gene pools? ☑

## Genetic Engineering (p.69-70) ☑

14) Give one risk associated with genetic engineering. ☑
15) What are restriction enzymes used for in genetic engineering? ☑
16) In genetic engineering, what is a vector? ☑

# Health and Disease

Try as we might, it's unlikely that we'll be in tip-top condition for all of our lives — <u>disease</u> tends to get us all at some point. There are lots of <u>different types</u> of diseases we could get...

## You Need to Know How 'Health' is Defined

1) It might surprise you to know that <u>being healthy</u> is about <u>more</u> than just <u>not being sick</u>.

2) The <u>World Health Organisation</u> (the <u>WHO</u>) defines health as "a state of <u>complete physical</u>, <u>mental</u> and <u>social well-being</u>, and not merely the absence of disease or infirmity".

3) This means that even if someone is very <u>physically fit</u>, they still might be <u>unhealthy</u> if, e.g. they have <u>mental health</u> issues or are <u>socially isolated</u>.

*Infirmity means weakness or frailness, commonly due to old age.*

## Diseases Can be Communicable or Non-Communicable

1) A disease is a <u>condition</u> where <u>part</u> of an organism <u>doesn't function</u> properly. There are <u>two sorts</u> of disease — <u>communicable</u> and <u>non-communicable</u>.

2) <u>Communicable diseases</u> are diseases that can be spread <u>between</u> individuals.

3) <u>Non-communicable diseases</u> can't be transmitted between individuals. They include things like <u>cancer</u> and <u>heart disease</u>. There's more on these on pages 83-84.

4) If you are affected by <u>one</u> disease, it could make you <u>more</u> <u>susceptible</u> to others — your body may become <u>weakened</u> by the disease, so it's less able to fight off others.

*Being susceptible to a disease, means that you have an increased chance of getting it.*

## Communicable Diseases are Caused by Pathogens

<u>Pathogens</u> are <u>organisms</u> such as <u>viruses</u>, <u>bacteria</u>, <u>fungi</u> and <u>protists</u> (see p.67) that cause <u>communicable diseases</u>. Here are some examples of <u>communicable diseases</u> that you need to know about for your exam:

## Chalara Ash Dieback is a Fungal Disease

1) Chalara ash dieback is caused by a <u>fungus</u> that infects ash trees.

2) Symptoms include <u>leaf loss</u> and <u>bark lesions</u> (wounds).

3) The fungus is carried through the <u>air</u> by the <u>wind</u>. (It also spreads when <u>diseased ash trees</u> are <u>moved</u> between areas.)

4) Transmission can be reduced by <u>removing young, infected ash trees</u> and <u>replanting</u> with different species or by <u>restricting</u> the <u>import</u> or <u>movement</u> of ash trees.

# Health and Disease

## Malaria is a Disease Caused by a **Protist**

1) The pathogen that causes malaria is a <u>protist</u>.
2) The effects of malaria include damage to <u>red blood cells</u> and, in severe cases, to the <u>liver</u>.
3) <u>Mosquitoes</u> act as animal <u>vectors</u> (carriers) — they pass on the <u>protist</u> to humans but don't get the disease <u>themselves</u>.
4) <u>Mosquito nets</u> and <u>insect repellent</u> can be used to prevent mosquitoes carrying the pathogen from <u>biting</u> people.

## Cholera is a **Bacterial** Disease

1) <u>Cholera</u> is a disease caused by a <u>bacterium</u> called *Vibrio cholerae*.
2) It causes diarrhoea.
3) Cholera spreads via contaminated <u>water</u> sources.
4) Transmission can be reduced by making sure that people have access to <u>clean water supplies</u>.

## Tuberculosis is a **Bacterial** Disease

1) <u>Tuberculosis</u> is caused by a <u>bacterium</u> called *Mycobacterium tuberculosis*.
2) It causes coughing and <u>lung damage</u>.
3) The bacteria are spread through the <u>air</u> when infected individuals cough.
4) Infected people should <u>avoid crowded public spaces</u>, <u>practise good hygiene</u> and <u>sleep alone</u>. Their homes should also be <u>well-ventilated</u>.

## Communicable diseases spread from one individual to another

In the exam, you could be asked how to <u>prevent the transmission</u> of a disease.
Remember, preventing the spread of a disease is linked to <u>how it spreads</u>. For example, if a disease is transmitted through contaminated water sources, then its spread can be prevented by making sure that individuals have access to clean water supplies.

# Sexually Transmitted Infections

Some communicable diseases are transmitted <u>sexually</u>.

## STIs are **Sexually Transmitted Infections**

<u>STIs</u> are infections that are spread through <u>sexual contact</u>, including <u>sexual intercourse</u>. Here are <u>two</u> STIs that you need to know about:

*Some STIs, including Chlamydia, are spread by genital contact, not just sexual intercourse.*

### Chlamydia

1) *Chlamydia* is a kind of <u>bacterium</u>, but it behaves in a similar way to a <u>virus</u> because it can only reproduce <u>inside host cells</u>.

2) Although it doesn't always cause <u>symptoms</u>, it can result in <u>infertility</u> in men and women.

3) The <u>spread</u> of *Chlamydia* can be <u>reduced</u> by wearing a <u>condom</u> when having sex, <u>screening</u> individuals so they can be <u>treated</u> for the infection or <u>avoiding sexual contact</u>.

### HIV

1) HIV is the <u>Human Immunodeficiency Virus</u> — it kills <u>white blood cells</u>, which are really important in the <u>immune response</u>.

2) HIV infection eventually leads to <u>AIDS</u> (Acquired Immune Deficiency Syndrome).

3) This is when the infected person's immune system <u>deteriorates</u> and eventually <u>fails</u> — because of this, the person becomes very <u>vulnerable</u> to opportunistic infections by <u>other pathogens</u>.

4) HIV is spread via infected <u>bodily fluids</u> (e.g. blood, semen, vaginal fluids). One of the main ways to prevent its spread is to use a <u>condom</u> when having sex. <u>Drug users</u> should also avoid <u>sharing needles</u>. <u>Medication</u> can <u>reduce the risk</u> of an infected individual passing the virus on to others during sex (or of a mother passing the virus to her baby during pregnancy) so <u>screening</u> and <u>proper treatment</u> are also important.

## Watch yourself, there are a lot of nasties out there...

Try drawing out a <u>table</u> with columns for 'disease', 'pathogen', 'symptom / effects', 'how it's spread' and 'how to reduce/prevent transmission', then fill it in for all the diseases on the previous three pages. See how much you can write down <u>without</u> looking back at the pages.

# Warm-Up and Exam Questions

Have a go at these questions to test what you've picked up about diseases — their symptoms, how they are transmitted and how their spread can be limited. You can go back over anything you struggle with.

## Warm-Up Questions

1) How does the World Health Organisation (WHO) define the term 'health'?
2) What does it mean if a disease is 'communicable'?
3) Name two diseases caused by bacteria.
4) How is HIV spread through sexual contact?
5) Give one way to reduce the spread of *Chlamydia*.

## Exam Questions

1    Chalara ash dieback is caused by a pathogen that infects ash trees.    **Grade 4-6**

(a)    Give the definition of the term 'pathogen'.

*[1 mark]*

(b)    What type of pathogen causes Chalara ash dieback?

☐    **A**    A bacterium

☐    **B**    A virus

☐    **C**    A protist

☐    **D**    A fungus

*[1 mark]*

(c)    Outline **one** way that Chalara ash dieback spreads.

*[1 mark]*

2    The methods used to prevent the spread of a disease depend on how the disease is transmitted.    **Grade 6-7**

(a)    Explain why hand washing may not be helpful in limiting the spread of malaria.

*[2 marks]*

(b)    Suggest and explain **one** reason why efforts to limit the spread of malaria often focus on the mosquito.

*[1 mark]*

Typhoid fever is a bacterial disease that infects humans. Typhoid fever is spread by eating or drinking food or water contaminated with the faeces of an infected person.

(c)    Suggest **one** way that the spread of typhoid fever could be reduced.

*[1 mark]*

# Fighting Disease

The human body has some pretty neat features when it comes to <u>fighting disease</u>.

## Physical and Chemical Barriers Stop Pathogens Entering the Body

The <u>human body</u> has <u>physical</u> and <u>chemical</u> defences against pathogen entry.

### Physical barriers

1) The skin acts as a <u>barrier</u> to pathogens, and, if it gets <u>damaged</u>, <u>blood clots</u> quickly <u>seal cuts</u> and keep microorganisms <u>out</u>.

2) <u>Hairs</u> and <u>mucus</u> in your nose <u>trap</u> particles that could contain <u>pathogens</u>.

3) <u>Cells</u> in your <u>trachea</u> and <u>bronchi</u> (airways in the lungs) also produce <u>mucus</u>, which traps pathogens. <u>Other cells</u> that line the trachea and bronchi have <u>cilia</u>. These are <u>hair-like structures</u> which waft the mucus up to the <u>back of the throat</u> where it can be <u>swallowed</u>.

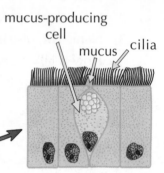

mucus-producing cell

mucus

cilia

### Chemical barriers

1) The <u>stomach</u> produces <u>hydrochloric acid</u>. This <u>kills</u> most pathogens that are swallowed.

2) The <u>eyes</u> produce a chemical called <u>lysozyme</u> (in tears) which <u>kills bacteria</u> on the <u>surface</u> of the eye.

*These physical and chemical barriers are non-specific — they work against many different types of pathogens.*

## Your Immune System Can Attack Pathogens

1) If pathogens do make it into your body, your <u>immune system</u> kicks in to <u>destroy</u> them.

2) The most important part of your immune system is the <u>white blood cells</u>. They travel around in your <u>blood</u> and crawl into every part of you, patrolling for <u>pathogens</u>.

3) <u>B-lymphocytes</u> are a type of white blood cell that are involved in the <u>specific immune response</u> — this is the immune response to a <u>specific pathogen</u>. Here's how it works:

1) Every pathogen has <u>unique molecules</u> (e.g. proteins) on its surface called <u>antigens</u>.

2) When your B-lymphocytes come across an antigen on a <u>pathogen</u>, they start to produce <u>proteins</u> called <u>antibodies</u>. Antibodies <u>bind</u> (lock on) to the new invading <u>pathogen</u>, so it can be <u>found</u> and <u>destroyed</u> by other white blood cells. The antibodies produced are <u>specific</u> to that pathogen — they won't lock on to any <u>other</u> pathogens.

3) The <u>antibodies</u> are then produced <u>rapidly</u> and flow all round the body to find all similar <u>pathogens</u>.

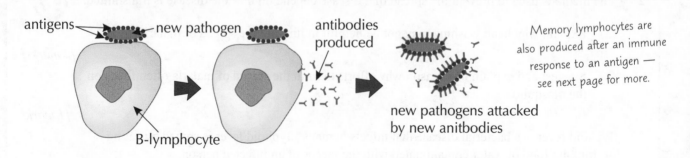

antigens

new pathogen

antibodies produced

B-lymphocyte

new pathogens attacked by new anitbodies

*Memory lymphocytes are also produced after an immune response to an antigen — see next page for more.*

## Antigens on the surfaces of pathogens trigger an immune response

If you have a low level of <u>white blood cells</u>, you'll be more susceptible to <u>infections</u>. HIV attacks white blood cells and <u>weakens</u> the immune system, making it easier for other pathogens to invade.

# Memory Lymphocytes

Our immune system contains special cells which can remember what pathogens have invaded our bodies in the past.  This means our bodies can respond faster if they invade again.

## Memory Lymphocytes Give Immunity To Later Infection

1) When a pathogen enters the body for the first time the response is slow because there aren't many B-lymphocytes that can make the antibody needed to lock on to the antigen.

2) Eventually the body will produce enough of the right antibody to overcome the infection.  Meanwhile the infected person will show symptoms of the disease.

3) As well as antibodies, memory lymphocytes are also produced in response to a foreign antigen.  Memory lymphocytes remain in the body for a long time, and 'remember' a specific antigen.

4) The person is now immune — their immune system has the ability to respond quickly to a second infection.

5) If the same pathogen enters the body again, there are more cells that will recognise it and produce antibodies against it.  This secondary immune response is faster and stronger.

6) The secondary response often gets rid of the pathogen before you begin to show any symptoms.

7) This can all be shown in a graph like the one here:

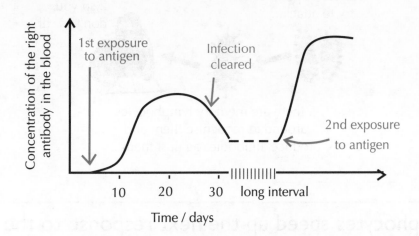

# Immunisation

Immunisation has changed the way we fight disease. We don't always have to deal with the problem once it's happened — we can <u>prevent</u> it happening in the first place.

## Immunisation Stops You Getting Infections

1)  To avoid getting ill, you can be <u>immunised</u> against some diseases, e.g. measles.

2)  <u>Immunisation</u> usually involves injecting <u>dead</u> or <u>inactive</u> pathogens into the body. These are <u>antigenic</u> (they carry antigens), so even though they're <u>harmless</u> your body makes <u>antibodies</u> to help destroy them.

3)  The antigens also trigger the production of <u>memory lymphocytes.</u>

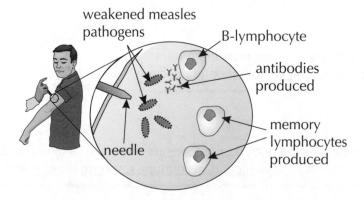

weakened measles pathogens
B-lymphocyte
antibodies produced
memory lymphocytes produced
needle

4)  So, if <u>live</u> pathogens of the <u>same type</u> get into the body, there will already be <u>memory lymphocytes</u> that can cause a fast <u>secondary immune response</u>. This means that you're less likely to get the disease.

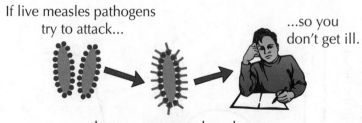

If live measles pathogens try to attack...

...so you don't get ill.

...there are memory lymphocytes around to recognise them and produce antibodies against them...

## Memory lymphocytes speed up the next response to the pathogen
<u>Immunisation</u> has helped to save millions of lives — and it's all because of <u>antibodies</u> and <u>memory cells</u>.

# Antibiotics and Other Medicines

New medicines are constantly being <u>developed</u>. This page tells you all about how that happens.

## Antibiotics Are Used to Treat Bacterial Infections

1) Antibiotics work by <u>inhibiting processes</u> in <u>bacterial cells</u>, but <u>not</u> in the <u>host organism</u>. For example, some antibiotics inhibit the <u>building</u> of bacterial <u>cell walls</u> — this <u>prevents</u> the bacteria from <u>dividing</u>, and eventually <u>kills them</u>, but has <u>no effect</u> on cells in the <u>human host</u> (which <u>don't</u> have cell walls).

2) <u>Different antibiotics</u> kill <u>different types</u> of bacteria, so it's important to be treated with the <u>right one</u>.

3) But antibiotics <u>don't destroy viruses</u> (e.g. <u>flu</u> or <u>cold</u> viruses). Viruses reproduce <u>using your body cells</u>, which makes it <u>very difficult</u> to develop drugs that destroy just the virus <u>without</u> killing the body's cells.

## There Are Several Stages in the Development of New Drugs

1) First a drug has to be <u>discovered</u>. This can happen in lots of different ways — for example:

> <u>Penicillin</u> is an <u>antibiotic</u>. It was discovered by Alexander Fleming when he was clearing out Petri dishes containing <u>bacteria</u>. He noticed that one of the dishes had <u>mould</u> on it and that the area around the mould was <u>free</u> of bacteria. The mould was producing <u>penicillin</u>, which was <u>killing</u> the bacteria.

2) Nowadays, most scientists use their knowledge of how a disease <u>works</u> to try and identify <u>molecules</u> that could be used as drugs to <u>fight</u> the disease.

3) Once a new potential drug has been <u>discovered</u>, it needs to be <u>developed</u>. This involves <u>preclinical</u> and <u>clinical testing</u>.

### Preclinical testing

1) In preclinical testing, drugs are <u>first</u> tested on <u>human cells and tissues</u> in the lab. However, you can't use human cells and tissues to test drugs that affect whole or multiple body systems, e.g. a drug for blood pressure must be tested on a whole animal.

2) The next step is to test the drug on <u>live animals</u>. This is to <u>test</u> that the drug <u>works</u> (produces the <u>effect</u> you're looking for), to find out how <u>toxic</u> (<u>harmful</u>) it is and to find the best <u>dosage</u>.

### Clinical testing

1) If the drug <u>passes</u> the tests on animals then it's tested on <u>human volunteers</u> in a <u>clinical trial</u>.

2) First, the drug is tested on <u>healthy volunteers</u> to make sure that it doesn't have any <u>harmful side effects</u> when the body is working <u>normally</u>.

3) If the results of the tests on healthy volunteers are good, the drugs can be tested on people suffering from the <u>illness</u>. The <u>optimum dose</u> is found — this is the dose of drug that is the <u>most effective</u> and has the <u>fewest side effects</u>.

4) Patients are <u>randomly</u> put into <u>two groups</u>. One is given the <u>new drug</u>, the other is given a <u>placebo</u> (a substance that <u>looks like</u> the drug being tested but <u>doesn't do anything</u>, e.g. a sugar pill). This is to allow for the <u>placebo effect</u> (when the patient expects the treatment to work and so <u>feels better</u>, even though the treatment isn't doing anything).

5) Clinical trials are <u>blind</u> — the patient in the study <u>doesn't know</u> whether they're getting the <u>drug</u> or the <u>placebo</u>. In fact, they're often <u>double-blind</u> — neither the <u>patient</u> nor the <u>doctor</u> knows until all the <u>results</u> have been gathered. This is so the doctors <u>monitoring</u> the patients and <u>analysing</u> the results aren't <u>subconsciously influenced</u> by their knowledge.

4) When a drug has finally passed all of these tests, it still needs to be <u>approved</u> by a <u>medical agency</u> before it can be used to <u>treat</u> patients. All of this means that drugs are as <u>effective</u> and <u>safe</u> as possible.

# Warm-Up and Exam Questions

It's that time again — time to test just how much of the previous pages you really remember...

Warm-Up Questions

1) How is the skin adapted to defend against the entry of pathogens?
2) What is the role of the specific immune system?
3) What type of white blood cell produces antibodies?
4) True or false?  Antibiotics kill viruses.
5) What is a placebo?

## Exam Questions

**1** There are many different lines of defence in the human body that help to prevent pathogens from entering the blood.  *Grade 4-6*

    (a) Give the role of mucus in the nose.

*[1 mark]*

    (b) Describe how the cilia in the trachea and bronchi help to defend the body.

*[1 mark]*

    (c) Name the substance produced by the stomach to kill pathogens.

*[1 mark]*

    (d) Name the chemical produced to kill bacteria on the surface of the eyes.

*[1 mark]*

**2** A scientist is carrying out a clinical trial.  *Grade 6-7*

    (a) What is a drug tested on in a clinical trial?

       ☐ **A** human cells

       ☐ **B** human volunteers

       ☐ **C** live animals

       ☐ **D** human tissue

*[1 mark]*

    (b) The clinical trial is double blind.  Explain what this means.

*[2 marks]*

When testing the drug on living organisms, the scientist has to find out how toxic the drug is by seeing whether it causes any harm.

    (c) Apart from the toxicity of the drug, suggest **two** other factors that scientists research during drug testing.

*[2 marks]*

# Non-Communicable Diseases

Non-communicable diseases aren't caused by pathogens. Instead, there are risk factors associated with them.

## Lifestyle Factors May Increase the Risk of Disease

1) Risk factors are things that are linked to an increase in the likelihood that a person will develop a certain disease during their lifetime. They don't guarantee that someone will get the disease.

2) Risk factors can be unavoidable, e.g. a person's age or gender may make them more likely to get a disease. But some are lifestyle factors that people can change. For example:

Smoking is a major risk factor associated with cardiovascular disease — any disease associated with the heart or blood vessels, e.g. a heart attack or stroke (see p.86). This is because:

- Nicotine in cigarette smoke increases heart rate, which increases blood pressure.
- High blood pressure damages artery walls, which contributes to the build up of fatty deposits in the arteries. These deposits restrict blood flow and increase the risk of a heart attack or stroke.
- Smoking increases the risk of blood clots forming in arteries, which can restrict or block blood flow, leading to a heart attack or stroke.

3) Other lifestyle factors are associated with different diseases. E.g.

A diet with too many or too few nutrients can lead to malnutrition (and diseases associated with malnutrition, e.g. scurvy — a vitamin C deficiency disease.)

Malnutrition doesn't just mean not getting enough nutrients. Getting too many nutrients is also a form of malnutrition, and it can lead to obesity.

Not getting enough exercise and having a diet high in fat and sugar are risk factors for obesity.

Drinking too much alcohol is a major risk factor for the development of liver disease, e.g. cirrhosis (scarring of the liver). This is because alcohol is broken down by enzymes in the liver and some of the products are toxic. Drinking too much over a long period of time can cause permanent liver damage.

## Non-communicable diseases don't spread between people

**EXAM TIP** In the exam, you might need to read data related to disease risk factors from a table, graph or chart, or explain what the data is showing. Remember to always check any units or graph scales carefully before answering any questions.

# Non-Communicable Diseases

You need to know about the effect of <u>lifestyle factors</u> on non-communicable diseases at different <u>levels</u>.

## Non-Communicable Diseases Have Many Risk Factors

1) As well as <u>smoking</u>, there are lots of other risk factors associated with <u>cardiovascular disease</u>, including: drinking too much <u>alcohol</u>, <u>lack of exercise</u>, and a diet <u>high</u> in saturated <u>fat</u>.

2) In fact, many <u>non-communicable</u> diseases are caused by <u>several different</u> risk factors <u>interacting</u> with each other, rather than <u>one factor alone</u>, including <u>cancer</u>, <u>liver</u> and <u>lung diseases</u> and <u>obesity</u>. <u>Obesity</u> is also a risk factor for <u>other</u> non-communicable diseases, e.g. <u>type 2 diabetes</u> (see p.111) and <u>cardiovascular disease</u>.

## Non-Communicable Diseases Can Have Wide-Ranging Effects

1) Non-communicable diseases can have <u>knock-on effects</u> for local areas. For example, in areas where there are <u>high levels</u> of <u>obesity</u>, <u>smoking</u> or <u>excess alcohol consumption</u>, there's likely to be a <u>high occurrence</u> of certain <u>non-communicable diseases</u>, e.g. cardiovascular or liver disease. This can put <u>pressure</u> on the <u>resources</u> (money, beds, staff, etc.) of <u>local hospitals</u>.

2) Non-communicable diseases are also costly at a <u>national level</u> because the <u>National Health Service</u> provides the <u>resources</u> for the treatment of patients all over the UK. And sometimes, people <u>suffering</u> from a non-communicable disease may not be able to <u>work</u>. A <u>reduction</u> in the number of people able to work can affect a country's <u>economy</u>.

3) As well as being costly, non-communicable diseases are <u>very common</u>, e.g. <u>cardiovascular disease</u> is the <u>number one</u> cause of death <u>worldwide</u>. In <u>developing countries</u>, <u>malnutrition</u> is also a big problem because people are not able to access <u>enough food</u>. The high cost and occurrence of these diseases can hold back the <u>development</u> of a <u>country</u> — so they have an effect at a <u>global</u> level.

## It's hard to avoid all risk factors of disease...

...but risk factors don't mean you'll <u>definitely</u> get the disease — they just increase the chance of getting it.

# Measures of Obesity

People come in all sorts of shapes and sizes, so you can't just say that anyone over a particular weight is obese. You have to use indices and ratios to figure this out instead — which is what this page is all about.

## A **Body Mass Index** Indicates If You're **Under-** or **Overweight**

1) The Body Mass Index (BMI) is used as a guide to help decide whether someone is underweight, normal, overweight or obese. It's calculated from their height and mass:

$$BMI = \frac{mass\ (kg)}{(height\ (m))^2}$$

| Body Mass Index | Weight Description |
|---|---|
| below 18.5 | underweight |
| 18.5 - 24.9 | normal |
| 25 - 29.9 | overweight |
| 30 - 40 | moderately obese |
| above 40 | severely obese |

2) Once you have a value for a person's BMI, you can refer to a table that shows how the different values are classified.

**EXAMPLE:** Calculate the BMI of a person who has a mass of 63.0 kg and is 1.70 m tall. Is this person overweight?

$BMI = \frac{mass\ (kg)}{(height\ (m))^2}$ = 63.0 kg ÷ 1.70 m² = 21.8 kg m⁻² This person is not overweight — their BMI lies between 18.5 and 24.9 (the normal mass range).

3) If you eat a high fat, high sugar diet and you don't do enough exercise, you're likely to take in more energy than you use. The excess energy is stored as fat, so you're more likely to have a high BMI and be obese.

4) BMI isn't always a reliable measure of obesity. For example, athletes have lots of muscle, which has a higher mass than fat, so they can come out with a high BMI even though they're not overweight.

## A **Waist-to-Hip Ratio** Can Also Be Used

1) By measuring the circumference of a person's waist and hips, you can use the following formula to figure out their waist-to-hip ratio.

$$waist\text{-}to\text{-}hip\ ratio = \frac{waist\ circumference}{hip\ circumference}$$

(e.g. in cm)
(e.g. in cm)

The circumference of a person's waist or hips is the distance the whole way around their body at that point.

2) The higher your waist-to-hip ratio, the more weight you're likely to be carrying around your middle.

3) A ratio above 1.0 for males and above 0.85 for females indicates you're carrying too much weight around your middle — this is known as abdominal obesity. It puts you at a greater risk of developing obesity-related health problems, such as type 2 diabetes (see p.111).

**EXAMPLE:** A woman has a waist measurement of 29 cm and a hip measurement of 36 cm. Find her waist-to-hip ratio.

$waist\text{-}to\text{-}hip\ ratio = \frac{waist\ circumference\ (cm)}{hip\ circumference\ (cm)}$ = 29 ÷ 36 = 0.81

## These measures of obesity aren't perfect...

However, they do provide a good guide for helping people know when it's time to lose weight.

# Treatments for Cardiovascular Disease

Cardiovascular disease is a <u>big, big problem</u> in the UK.  The good news is there are lots of ways to <u>treat</u> it.

## Cardiovascular Disease Affects Your Heart and Blood Vessels

Cardiovascular disease (<u>CVD</u>) is any disease associated with your <u>heart</u> and <u>blood vessels</u>.

1) Arteries are <u>blood vessels</u> that carry blood <u>away</u> from the <u>heart</u>.

*See p.122-123 for more on blood vessels and the heart.*

2) <u>Cholesterol</u> is a <u>fatty substance</u> that the body needs to make things like <u>cell membranes</u>.  But <u>too much</u> cholesterol in the blood can cause <u>fatty deposits</u> to build up in <u>arteries</u>, <u>restricting blood flow</u>.

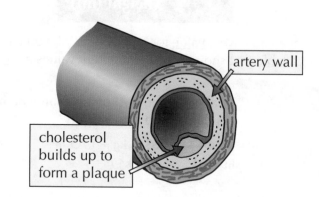

artery wall

cholesterol builds up to form a plaque

3) Deposits occur in areas where the <u>artery wall</u> has been <u>damaged</u>, e.g. by <u>high blood pressure</u>.

4) The fatty deposits can also trigger <u>blood clots</u> to form, which can <u>block blood flow</u> completely.  If this happens in an <u>artery</u> supplying the <u>heart muscle</u>, the heart muscle will be <u>deprived of oxygen</u>.  This causes a <u>heart attack</u>. A blockage in the <u>brain</u> deprives the brain of oxygen and can cause a <u>stroke</u>.

## Lifestyle Changes Can be Used to Treat CVD

1) Making <u>changes</u> to your <u>lifestyle</u> can <u>reduce your risk</u> of <u>developing CVD</u>. If you already <u>have CVD</u>, these changes can form part of the <u>treatment</u>, helping to <u>reduce the risk</u> of a <u>further heart attack</u> or <u>stroke</u>.

2) People with (or at risk of) CVD may be encouraged to eat a <u>healthy, balanced diet</u>, which is <u>low</u> in <u>saturated fat</u> (as saturated fat can increase blood cholesterol level). They may also be encouraged to <u>exercise</u> regularly, <u>lose weight</u> if necessary and stop <u>smoking</u>.

3) Lifestyle changes are often recommended <u>first</u> because they don't really have any <u>downsides</u>.

---

## Cardiovascular disease is associated with blood flow

Other factors, such as age, gender and family history can also <u>increase the risk</u> of developing CVD. These factors <u>can't</u> be changed, but it <u>is</u> possible to <u>control and modify</u> lifestyle-related risk factors.

# Treatments for Cardiovascular Disease

Lifestyle changes aren't always enough to treat CVD.  Sometimes medicine or surgery is needed too.

## Some **Drugs** Can **Reduce** the **Risk** of a **Heart Attack** or **Stroke**

Lifestyle changes aren't always <u>enough</u> to treat CVD.  Sometimes <u>medicines</u> are needed too.
<u>Some people</u> may need to take these medicines for the <u>rest of their lives</u>.

1) <u>Statins reduce</u> the amount of <u>cholesterol</u> in the <u>bloodstream</u>.  This <u>slows down</u> the rate at which fatty deposits form — <u>reducing</u> the risk of <u>heart attacks</u> and <u>strokes</u>.  However, they can sometimes cause <u>negative side effects</u>, e.g. aching muscles.  Some of these side effects can be <u>serious</u>, e.g. liver damage.

2) <u>Anticoagulants</u> (e.g. Warfarin™) are drugs which make <u>blood clots less likely to form</u>. However, this can cause excessive <u>bleeding</u> if the person is hurt in an <u>accident</u>.

3) <u>Antihypertensives</u> reduce <u>blood pressure</u>.  This helps to <u>prevent damage</u> to <u>blood vessels</u> and so reduces the risk of <u>fatty deposits</u> forming. However, they can cause <u>side effects</u>, e.g. headaches and fainting.

## **Surgical Procedures** are Sometimes **Necessary** to **Repair Damage**

1) Stents are <u>tubes</u> that are inserted <u>inside arteries</u>.  They keep them <u>open</u>, making sure <u>blood can pass through</u> to the heart muscles, <u>lowering</u> the <u>risk</u> of a <u>heart attack</u>. But <u>over time</u>, the artery can <u>narrow</u> again as stents can <u>irritate</u> the artery and make <u>scar tissue</u> grow.  The patient also has to take <u>drugs</u> to stop <u>blood clotting</u> on the stent.

2) If part of a blood vessel is <u>blocked</u>, a piece of <u>healthy vessel</u> taken from elsewhere can be used to <u>bypass</u> the blocked section.  This is known as <u>coronary bypass surgery</u>.

3) The whole heart can be replaced with a <u>donor heart</u>.  However, the new heart does not always start <u>pumping</u> properly and <u>drugs</u> have to be taken to stop the body <u>rejecting</u> it. These drugs can have <u>side effects</u>, e.g. making you more vulnerable to infections.

Any heart surgery is a <u>major procedure</u> and there is risk of <u>bleeding</u>, <u>clots</u> and <u>infection</u>.

## Don't lose heart...

**EXAM TIP**

You could be asked to <u>evaluate</u> treatments for <u>cardiovascular disease</u>.  Don't panic — just use any information you're given and your own knowledge to weigh up the <u>advantages</u> and <u>disadvantages</u>.  Make sure your answer doesn't just focus on <u>one side</u> — e.g. don't just talk about the advantages and ignore the disadvantages — and don't forget to include a justified <u>conclusion</u>.

# Warm-Up and Exam Questions

It's time for some more questions — don't just assume that you've remembered everything you read on the past few pages. Give these a go, and then go back over anything that you struggled with.

## Warm-Up Questions

1) Give an example of a national cost associated with non-communicable diseases in the UK.
2) Give one disadvantage of the body mass index (BMI) as a measure of obesity.
3) Give one advantage of making lifestyle changes as treatment for CVD.

## Exam Questions

1   Many non-communicable diseases are associated with certain lifestyle factors.

(a)   Give **one** lifestyle factor associated with liver disease.

*[1 mark]*

(b)   Give **one** example of a cost to the local area associated with liver disease.

*[1 mark]*

2   Cardiovascular disease is non-communicable.

(a)   Describe what is meant by the term 'non-communicable disease'.

*[1 mark]*

(b)   Explain how smoking increases a person's risk of cardiovascular disease.

*[4 marks]*

3   Before beginning a new diet and exercise routine, a person has a mass of 76.0 kg and has a height of 1.58 m. Three weeks later their mass has dropped to 73.0 kg.

(a)   Calculate the person's BMI at:

(i) The beginning of the three week period.

*[1 mark]*

(ii) The end of the three week period.

*[1 mark]*

(b)   Use **Figure 1** to determine the weight description of the person before and after the three week period.

| Body Mass Index | Weight Description |
|---|---|
| below 18.5 | underweight |
| 18.5 - 24.9 | normal |
| 25 - 29.9 | overweight |
| 30 - 40 | moderately obese |
| above 40 | severely obese |

**Figure 1**

*[2 marks]*

# Revision Summary for Topic 5

Well, that's Topic 5 finished.  Now it's time to test how much you've taken in...
- Try these questions and tick off each one when you get it right.
- When you've done all the questions under a heading and are completely happy, tick it off.

## Health, Disease, and STIs (p.74-76) ☑

1) Explain why being healthy doesn't just mean not being sick. ☑
2) True or False?  Non-communicable diseases are caused by pathogens. ☑
3) How can the transmission of malaria be prevented? ☑
4) Name a sexually transmitted infection (STI) caused by a bacterium. ☑
5) Why does HIV eventually lead to AIDS? ☑

## Fighting Disease and Immunisation (p.78-80) ☑

6) Give two types of chemical defence that prevent pathogens from infecting humans. ☑
7) What is an antigen? ☑
8) What does a B-lymphocyte do when it recognises a pathogen? ☑
9) How do vaccines prepare the immune system against infection by a particular pathogen? ☑

## Antibiotics and Other Medicines (p.81) ☑

10) Which type of pathogen can antibiotics be used to kill? ☑
11) What is the placebo effect? ☑

## Non-Communicable Diseases (p.83-87) ☑

12) Give two risk factors related to lifestyle associated with obesity. ☑
13) Write the equation for finding the body mass index of an individual. ☑
14) Give three examples of lifestyle changes that can help to prevent cardiovascular disease. ☑

# Photosynthesis

Photosynthesis is where energy enters most of the food chains on Earth. Organisms that can carry out photosynthesis have crucial positions at the start of those food chains.

## Plants are Able to Make Their Own Food by Photosynthesis

1) During photosynthesis, photosynthetic organisms, such as green plants and algae, use energy from the Sun to make glucose.

2) Some of the glucose is used to make larger, complex molecules that the plants or algae need to grow. These make up the organism's biomass — the mass of living material.

3) The energy stored in the organisms' biomass then works its way through the food chain as animals eat them and each other. So photosynthetic organisms are the main producers of food for nearly all life on Earth.

4) Photosynthesis happens inside chloroplasts — they contain chlorophyll which absorbs light. Energy is transferred to the chloroplasts by light. This is the equation for photosynthesis:

$$\text{carbon dioxide} + \text{water} \xrightarrow[\text{chlorophyll}]{\text{light}} \text{glucose} + \text{oxygen}$$
$$6CO_2 + 6H_2O \xrightarrow[\text{chlorophyll}]{\text{light}} C_6H_{12}O_6 + 6O_2$$

5) Photosynthesis is an endothermic reaction — energy is taken in during the reaction.

6) The rate of photosynthesis is affected by the light intensity, the concentration of $CO_2$ and the temperature. Any of these three factors can become the limiting factor. This just means that it's stopping photosynthesis from happening any faster.

## The TEMPERATURE has to be Just Right for Photosynthesis

Temperature affects the rate of photosynthesis because it affects the enzymes involved.

1) Usually, if the temperature is the limiting factor it's because it's too low — the enzymes needed for photosynthesis work more slowly at low temperatures.

2) But if the plant gets too hot, the enzymes it needs for photosynthesis and its other reactions will be denatured (see page 27).

3) This happens at about 45 °C (which is pretty hot for outdoors, although greenhouses can get that hot if you're not careful).

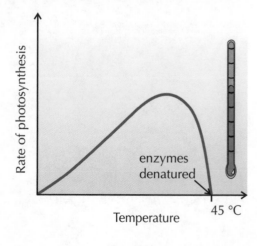

enzymes denatured

45 °C

# Photosynthesis

## Not Enough LIGHT Slows Down the Rate of Photosynthesis

1) Light transfers the <u>energy</u> needed for photosynthesis.

2) At first, as the <u>light level</u> is raised, the rate of photosynthesis <u>increases steadily</u> (the rate is <u>directly proportional</u> to light intensity). But this is only true up to a <u>certain point</u>.

3) Beyond that, it <u>won't</u> make any difference — it'll be either the <u>temperature</u> or the <u>$CO_2$ level</u> which is the limiting factor.

4) In the lab you can investigate light intensity by <u>moving</u> a <u>lamp</u> closer to or further away from your plant (see next page).

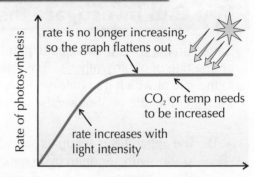

*rate is no longer increasing, so the graph flattens out*

*$CO_2$ or temp needs to be increased*

*rate increases with light intensity*

Rate of photosynthesis / Light intensity

5) But if you just plot the rate of photosynthesis against "distance of lamp from the plant", you get a <u>weird-shaped graph</u>. To get a graph like the one above you either need to <u>measure</u> the light intensity at the plant using a <u>light meter</u> or do a bit of maths with your results. Here's why:

The square of the distance from the lamp and the light intensity are <u>inversely proportional</u> to each other — this means as the <u>distance increases</u>, the <u>light intensity decreases</u>. However, light intensity decreases in proportion to the <u>square</u> of the distance. This is called the <u>inverse square law</u> and is written like this:

*∝ is the 'proportional to' symbol.*

$$\text{light intensity} \propto \frac{1}{\text{distance (d)}^2}$$

6) The inverse square law means that if you <u>halve</u> the <u>distance</u>, the <u>light intensity</u> will be <u>four times greater</u>. And if you <u>double</u> the distance, the light intensity will be <u>four times smaller</u>. (Trebling the distance would make it <u>nine times smaller</u>.) You can use $1/d^2$ as a measure of light intensity:

### EXAMPLE:
**Using the inverse square law, calculate the light intensity at both 20 cm and 10 cm from a lamp.**

1) Use the <u>formula</u> for calculating light intensity.

*'a.u.' stands for 'arbitrary units'.*

$$\text{light intensity} = \frac{1}{d^2}$$

2) For each of the distances, put the value into the formula, then <u>calculate the answer</u>.

At 20 cm: light intensity $= \dfrac{1}{20^2} = \dfrac{1}{400} = 0.0025$ a.u

At 10 cm: light intensity $= \dfrac{1}{10^2} = \dfrac{1}{100} = 0.0100$ a.u.

<u>Halving</u> the distance has made the light intensity <u>four times</u> greater.

## Too Little CARBON DIOXIDE Slows Photosynthesis Down

1) $CO_2$ is one of the <u>raw materials</u> needed for photosynthesis.

2) As with light intensity, increasing the <u>$CO_2$</u> concentration <u>increases</u> the rate of photosynthesis up to a point. After this the graph <u>flattens out</u>, showing that $CO_2$ is no longer the <u>limiting factor</u>.

3) As long as <u>$CO_2$</u> is in plentiful supply then light or temperature is the factor limiting photosynthesis.

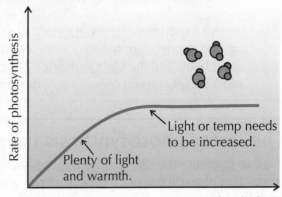

*Light or temp needs to be increased.*

*Plenty of light and warmth.*

Rate of photosynthesis / % level of $CO_2$

Topic 6 — Plant Structures and Their Functions

## PRACTICAL Investigating Photosynthesis

It's practical time again. This one lets you see how changing <u>light intensity</u> affects the <u>rate of photosynthesis</u>.

## You Can Investigate the Rate of Photosynthesis

<u>Canadian pondweed</u> (an aquatic plant) can be used to measure the effect of <u>light intensity</u> on the <u>rate of photosynthesis</u>. The rate at which the pondweed produces <u>oxygen</u> corresponds to the rate at which it's photosynthesising — the <u>faster</u> the rate of oxygen production, the <u>faster</u> the rate of photosynthesis. Here's how the experiment works:

1) The <u>apparatus</u> is <u>set up</u> as shown in the <u>diagram</u> below. The gas syringe should be empty to start with. <u>Sodium hydrogencarbonate</u> may be added to the water to make sure the plant has enough <u>carbon dioxide</u> (sodium hydrogencarbonate releases $CO_2$ in solution).

2) A source of <u>white light</u> is placed at a <u>specific distance</u> from the pondweed.

3) The pondweed is left to photosynthesise for a <u>set amount of time</u>.

This experiment can be modified to test the effect of temperature or carbon dioxide concentration too — just remember to only change one variable at a time.

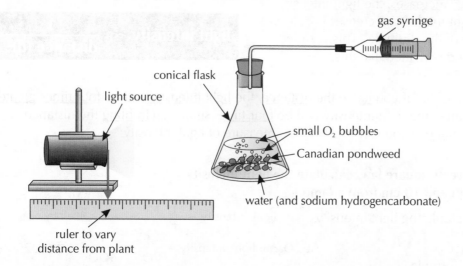

gas syringe

conical flask

light source

small $O_2$ bubbles

Canadian pondweed

water (and sodium hydrogencarbonate)

ruler to vary distance from plant

You can also investigate the rate of photosynthesis using algal balls, instead of pondweed. These are little balls of jelly which contain algae.

4) As it photosynthesises, the oxygen released will collect in the <u>gas syringe</u>. This allows you to <u>accurately measure</u> the <u>volume</u> of oxygen produced.

5) The whole experiment is repeated with the <u>light source</u> at <u>different distances</u> from the pondweed. The <u>rate of oxygen production</u> at each distance can then be calculated (volume produced ÷ time taken).

You could measure how much oxygen is produced by counting the number of bubbles given off in a certain time instead — but this is less accurate.

6) For this experiment, any <u>variables</u> that could affect the results should be <u>controlled</u>, e.g. the <u>temperature</u> (which can be controlled by putting the conical flask in a <u>water bath</u>) and the <u>carbon dioxide concentration</u> (which can be controlled by adding a <u>set amount</u> of sodium hydrogencarbonate to a <u>set volume</u> of water).

## The faster photosynthesis happens, the faster oxygen is produced

You can <u>compare</u> the <u>rate of photosynthesis</u> at different light intensities by comparing the <u>rate of oxygen production</u> (the volume of $O_2$ produced per unit time e.g. in $cm^3$ $min^{-1}$). Increasing light intensity <u>increases</u> the rate of oxygen production (but only until temperature or $CO_2$ become the limiting factor instead).

Topic 6 — Plant Structures and Their Functions

# Warm-Up & Exam Questions

Time for a break in the topic and some questions. Do them now, whilst all that learning is fresh in your mind. Using that knowledge will help you to remember it all, and that's what this game is all about.

## Warm-Up Questions

1) True or false? Photosynthesis is an exothermic reaction.
2) What is meant by a limiting factor for the rate of photosynthesis?
3) Explain why the rate of photosynthesis decreases if the temperature is too high.
4) Write down the inverse square law for light intensity.

## Exam Questions

**PRACTICAL**

1    A student did an experiment to see how the rate of photosynthesis **Grade 4-6** depends on light intensity. **Figure 1** shows some of her apparatus.

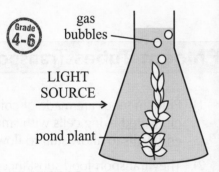

**Figure 1**

(a)    Suggest how the student could measure the rate of photosynthesis.

*[1 mark]*

(b)    State the dependent variable and the independent variable in this experiment.

*[2 marks]*

2    The graph in **Figure 2** shows how changing the light intensity affected the rate of photosynthesis of a plant.

During the experiment, the plant was kept at a constant temperature and a constant concentration of carbon dioxide.

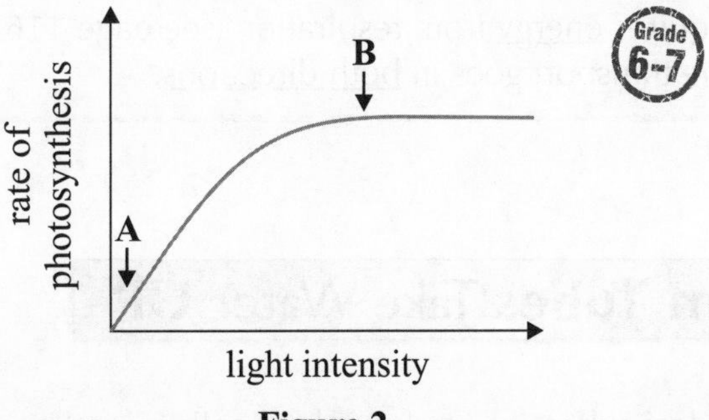

**Figure 2**

(a)    State what factor was limiting the rate of photosynthesis of the plant between points **A** and **B** on the graph. Explain your answer.

*[2 marks]*

(b)    Explain why the graph flattens off after point **B**.

*[2 marks]*

3    A student is investigating the effect of light intensity on the rate of photosynthesis by placing **Grade 7-9** a lamp at various distances from a plant and measuring the rate of photosynthesis.

Use the inverse square law to calculate the light intensity when the lamp is 7.5 cm from the plant. Give your answer in arbitrary units (a.u.) to 2 significant figures.

*[2 marks]*

# Transport in Plants

Plants need to get stuff from <u>A to B</u>.  Flowering plants have <u>two types</u> of <u>transport vessel</u> — <u>xylem</u> and <u>phloem</u>.  Both types of vessel go to <u>every part</u> of the plant, but they are totally <u>separate</u>.

## Root Hairs Take In Minerals and Water

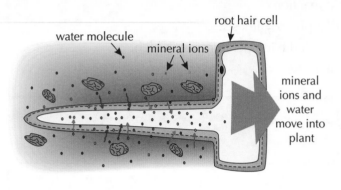

water molecule

mineral ions

root hair cell

mineral ions and water move into plant

1) The cells on the surface of plant roots grow into "hairs", which stick out into the soil.

2) Each branch of a root will be covered in <u>millions</u> of these microscopic hairs.

3) This gives the plant a <u>large surface area</u> for absorbing <u>water</u> and <u>mineral ions</u> from the soil.

4) The concentration of mineral ions is usually <u>higher</u> in the <u>root hair cells</u> than in the <u>soil</u> around them, so mineral ions are absorbed by <u>active transport</u> (see page 32).

5) Water is absorbed by <u>osmosis</u>.

## Phloem Tubes Transport Food

1) Phloem tubes are made of columns of <u>elongated</u> living cells with small <u>pores</u> in the <u>end walls</u> to allow stuff to flow through.

2) They transport <u>food substances</u> (mainly <u>sucrose</u>) made in the leaves to the rest of the plant for <u>immediate use</u> (e.g. in growing regions) or for <u>storage</u>.

3) This process is called <u>translocation</u> and it requires <u>energy</u> from respiration (see page 116). The transport goes in <u>both directions</u>.

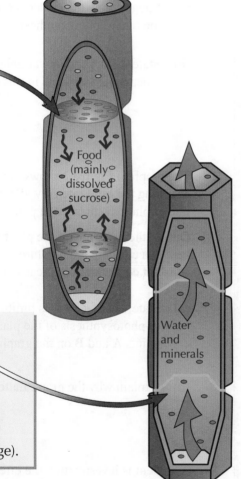

Food (mainly dissolved sucrose)

Water and minerals

## Xylem Tubes Take Water UP

1) Xylem tubes are made of <u>dead cells</u> joined end to end with <u>no</u> end walls between them and a hole down the middle. They're strengthened with a material called <u>lignin</u>.

2) They carry <u>water</u> and <u>mineral ions</u> from the <u>roots</u> to the <u>stem</u> and <u>leaves</u>.

3) The movement of water <u>from</u> the <u>roots</u>, <u>through</u> the <u>xylem</u> and <u>out</u> of the <u>leaves</u> is called the <u>transpiration stream</u> (see next page).

**REVISION TIP**

## Xylem vessels carry water, phloem vessels carry sucrose

Make sure you don't get your phloem <u>mixed up</u> with your xylem.  To help you to learn which is which, you could remember that phl<u>o</u>em transports substances in b<u>o</u>th directions, but xylem only transports things upwards — x<u>y</u> to the sky.  It might just bag you a mark or two on exam day...

# Transpiration and Stomata

Plants need <u>water</u> and <u>gases</u> such as carbon dioxide and oxygen.

## Transpiration is the **Loss of Water** from the Plant

1) Transpiration is caused by the <u>evaporation</u> and <u>diffusion</u> (see p.32) of water from a plant's surface. Most transpiration happens at the <u>leaves</u>.

2) The loss of water creates a slight <u>shortage</u> of water in the leaf, and so more water is drawn up from the rest of the plant through the <u>xylem vessels</u> to replace it.

3) This in turn means more water is drawn up from the <u>roots</u>, and so there's a constant <u>transpiration stream</u> of water through the plant.

4) The transpiration stream carries <u>mineral ions</u> that are dissolved in the water along with it.

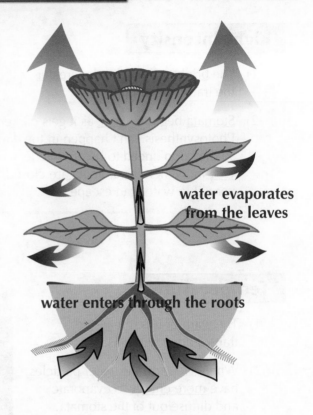

**water evaporates from the leaves**

**water enters through the roots**

## Stomata are Needed for **Gas Exchange**

1) Stomata are <u>tiny pores</u> on the surface of a plant. They're mostly found on the lower surface of <u>leaves</u>. Stomata allow <u>CO$_2$</u> and <u>oxygen</u> to <u>diffuse</u> directly in and out of a leaf. They also allow <u>water vapour</u> to escape during <u>transpiration</u>.

It's one stoma, but two or more stomata.

2) Transpiration is really just a <u>side-effect</u> of the way leaves are adapted for <u>photosynthesis</u>. They have to have <u>stomata</u> so that gases can be exchanged easily. Because there's more water <u>inside</u> the plant than in the <u>air outside</u>, the water escapes from the leaves through the stomata by diffusion.

3) Stomata are surrounded by <u>guard cells</u>, which <u>change shape</u> to control the size of the pore — when the guard cells are <u>turgid</u> (swollen with water) the stomata are <u>open</u> and when the guard cells are <u>flaccid</u> (low on water and limp) the stomata are <u>closed</u>.

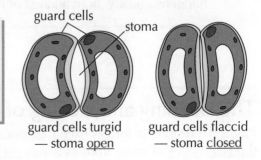

guard cells

stoma

guard cells turgid — stoma <u>open</u>

guard cells flaccid — stoma <u>closed</u>

# Transpiration Rate

The rate of transpiration varies according to the environmental conditions.

## Transpiration Rate is Affected by Environmental Factors

### Light Intensity

1) The brighter the light, the greater the transpiration rate.

2) Stomata begin to close as it gets darker. Photosynthesis can't happen in the dark, so they don't need to be open to let $CO_2$ in. When the stomata are closed, very little water can escape.

### Temperature

1) The warmer it is, the faster transpiration happens.

2) When it's warm the water particles have more energy to evaporate and diffuse out of the stomata.

The faster the transpiration rate, the faster the water uptake by the plant.

### Air Flow

1) The better the air flow around a leaf (e.g. stronger wind), the greater the transpiration rate.

2) If air flow around a leaf is poor, the water vapour just surrounds the leaf and doesn't move away. This means there's a high concentration of water particles outside the leaf as well as inside it, so diffusion doesn't happen as quickly.

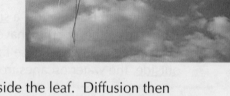

3) If there's good air flow, the water vapour is swept away, maintaining a low concentration of water in the air outside the leaf. Diffusion then happens quickly, from an area of higher concentration to an area of lower concentration.

## The opening and closing of stomata is important for plants to survive

Plants need stomata for gas exchange but they let out a lot of water too. A big tree can lose about a thousand litres of water from its leaves every single day. That's a lot of water, which is why closing the stomata in certain conditions (e.g at night) is really important to stop too much water being lost.

# Transpiration Rate

Sorry, more on <u>transpiration</u>, but at least this page is about a <u>practical</u>.

## You Can **Estimate Transpiration Rate**

You can use a special piece of apparatus called a <u>potometer</u> to <u>estimate transpiration rate</u>.
It actually <u>measures water uptake</u> by a plant, but it's <u>assumed</u> that water uptake by the plant is
<u>directly related</u> to water loss from the leaves (transpiration). Here's what you do:

1) Set up the apparatus as in the diagram, and then record the <u>starting position</u> of the air bubble.

2) Start a stopwatch and record the <u>distance moved</u> by the bubble per unit time, e.g. per hour.
Calculating the <u>speed</u> of <u>air bubble movement</u> gives an <u>estimate</u> of the <u>transpiration rate</u>.

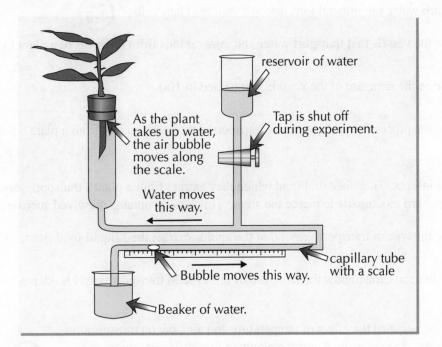

As the plant takes up water, the air bubble moves along the scale.

reservoir of water

Tap is shut off during experiment.

Water moves this way.

Bubble moves this way.

capillary tube with a scale

Beaker of water.

 **EXAMPLE:**

**A potometer was used to estimate the transpiration rate of a plant cutting.
The bubble moved 25 mm in 10 minutes. Estimate the transpiration rate.**

To estimate the <u>rate of transpiration</u>, divide the <u>distance</u> the bubble moved by the <u>time taken</u>.

$$\frac{distance\ moved}{time\ taken} = \frac{25\ mm}{10\ min} = 2.5\ mm\ min^{-1}$$

mm min⁻¹ is the same as mm/min.

You can use a potometer to estimate how <u>light intensity</u>, <u>temperature</u> or <u>air flow</u> around the plant
affect the transpiration rate. Just remember to <u>only change one variable at a time</u> and control the rest.

 **EXAM TIP**

## Make sure you know how to work out transpiration rate

You need to know how to <u>calculate</u> the rate of transpiration using measurements taken in a
practical like the one above. Watch out for the <u>units</u> — you might be asked to use different ones in
the exam. Don't panic though, just make sure your units match all the way through the calculation.

# Warm-Up & Exam Questions

There's a fair few diagrams on the previous pages. Make sure you familiarise yourself with the labels and content of each one, don't just look at the pretty colours... Anyway you know what's next by now...

## Warm-Up Questions

1) Where are most of a plant's stomata located?
2) True or false? Substances pass in both directions through xylem vessels.
3) State the three main factors that affect the rate of transpiration in plants.

## Exam Questions

1   Plants absorb water and mineral ions through their root hair cells.

   (a)   Name the vessels that transport water and mineral ions from the roots of a plant to the leaves.

   *[1 mark]*

   (b)   Describe the structure of the vessels you named in **1(a)**.

   *[3 marks]*

   (c)   Name the process by which water is transported through and lost from a plant.

   *[1 mark]*

2   Aphids are insects. They feed on liquid which they extract from a plant's transport vessels,
   using their sharp mouthparts to pierce the stem. This liquid contains dissolved sucrose.

   (a)   Name the type of transport vessel that the aphids extract their liquid food from.

   *[1 mark]*

   (b)   Describe and explain how the structure of this type of transport vessel is adapted to its function.

   *[4 marks]*

3   A student investigated the effect of temperature and air flow on transpiration
   in basil plants. She put groups of three plants in four different conditions.
   She weighed the plants before and after the experiment and calculated
   the % loss in mass for each plant. Her results are shown in **Figure 1**.

| plant | % loss in mass | | | |
| | Group A: 20 °C Still Room | Group B: 20 °C Next to a Fan | Group C: 25 °C Still Room | Group D: 25 °C Next to a Fan |
| --- | --- | --- | --- | --- |
| 1 | 5 | 8 | 10 | 13 |
| 2 | 5 | 9 | 11 | 15 |
| 3 | 4 | 11 | 9 | 13 |
| mean | 4.7 | 9.3 | | 13.6 |

**Figure 1**

   (a)   Calculate the mean % loss in mass for the three plants in Group **C**.

   *[2 marks]*

   (b)*  Explain why keeping the plants in Group **D** at 25 °C and placing them next to a fan
         meant that they lost more mass than the plants in Group **A**.

   *[6 marks]*

# Revision Summary for Topic 6

<u>Plants</u>, <u>plants</u> and more <u>plants</u> — that pretty much sums up <u>Topic 6</u> for you.

- Try these questions and <u>tick off each one</u> when you <u>get it right</u>.
- When you've done <u>all the questions</u> under a heading and are <u>completely happy</u>, tick it off.

## Photosynthesis and Limiting Factors (p.90-92) ☑

1) In what part of a cell does photosynthesis take place?
2) Apart from water vapour, what gas is needed for photosynthesis?
3) Name the two products of photosynthesis.
4) Why is photosynthesis described as an endothermic reaction?
5) Describe the relationship between light intensity and distance from a light source.
6) What effect would a low carbon dioxide concentration have on the rate of photosynthesis?
7) Describe how you could investigate the effect of light intensity on the rate of photosynthesis.

## Transport in Plants and Transpiration (p.94-97) ☑

8) How are root hair cells adapted to their function?
9) By what process do phloem tubes transport sucrose around a plant?
10) What effect does a faster transpiration rate have on water uptake by the plant?
11) a) What are stomata?
    b) What is the role of stomata in transpiration?
12) How does light intensity affect the rate of transpiration?
13) Describe how you'd use a potometer to estimate the rate of transpiration.

# Hormones

Way back in Topic 2 you learnt how information is passed around the body via <u>neurones</u>. Well the body also uses <u>hormones</u> as a way to communicate, which is what this page is all about.

## Hormones Are **Chemical Messengers** Sent in the **Blood**

1) <u>Hormones</u> are <u>chemical molecules</u> released directly into the <u>blood</u>.

2) They are carried in the blood to other parts of the body, but only affect particular cells in particular organs (called <u>target organs</u>).

3) Hormones control things in organs and cells that need <u>constant adjustment</u>.

4) Hormones are produced in (and secreted by) various <u>glands</u>, called <u>endocrine glands</u>. These glands make up your <u>endocrine system</u>.

## Endocrine Glands Are Found in **Different Places** in the Body

### PITUITARY GLAND

1) The pituitary gland produces <u>many hormones</u> that regulate <u>body conditions</u>.

2) It is sometimes called the '<u>master gland</u>' because these hormones act on <u>other glands</u>, directing them to <u>release hormones</u> that bring about <u>change</u>.

### THYROID

This produces <u>thyroxine</u>, which is involved in regulating things like the <u>rate of metabolism</u>, <u>heart rate</u> and <u>temperature</u> (see page 102) .

### ADRENAL GLAND

This produces <u>adrenaline</u>, which is used to prepare the body for a '<u>fight or flight</u>' response (see page 102).

### OVARIES (females only)

Produce <u>oestrogen</u>, which is involved in the <u>menstrual cycle</u> (see pages 104-105).

### PANCREAS

This produces <u>insulin</u>, which is used to regulate the <u>blood glucose level</u> (see page 110).

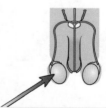

### TESTES (males only)

Produce <u>testosterone</u>, which controls <u>puberty</u> and <u>sperm production</u> in males.

# Comparing Neurones and Hormones

Now you know that there are <u>two</u> ways information can be sent round the body — via the <u>nervous</u> or <u>hormonal</u> systems — here's a page comparing the differences between them...

## Hormones and Nerves Carry Messages in Different Ways

<u>Hormones</u> and <u>nerves</u> do similar jobs — they both <u>carry information</u> and <u>instructions</u> around the body. But there are some important <u>differences</u> between them:

**Nerves**

Very <u>FAST</u> action.

Act for a very <u>SHORT TIME</u>.

Act on a very <u>PRECISE AREA</u>.

**Hormones**

<u>SLOWER</u> action.

Act for a <u>LONG TIME</u>.

Act in a more <u>GENERAL</u> way.

If you're not sure whether a response is nervous or hormonal, have a think about the <u>speed</u> of the reaction and <u>how long it lasts</u>.

## If the Response is Really Quick, It's Probably Nervous

1) Some information needs to be passed to effectors <u>really quickly</u>. For example:

- Signals telling you that a part of your body is feeling <u>pain</u> (so you can take action <u>quickly</u> to avoid your body being damaged).
- Information from your eyes telling you there's something <u>dangerous</u> heading your way.

2) It's no good using hormones to carry messages like these — they would be <u>too slow</u>.

## If a Response Lasts For a Long Time, It's Probably Hormonal

<u>Hormonal responses</u> tend to carry on having an effect for a <u>longer time</u> than nervous responses.

For example, when you get a <u>shock</u>, a hormone called <u>adrenaline</u> is released into the body (causing the fight or flight response, where your body is hyped up ready for action). You can tell it's a <u>hormonal response</u> (even though it kicks in pretty quickly) because you feel a bit wobbly for a while <u>afterwards</u>.

There's more about adrenaline on the next page.

## Nerves, hormones — no wonder revision makes me tense...

Hormones control various organs and cells in the body, though they tend to control things that <u>aren't immediately life-threatening</u> (so things like <u>sexual development</u>, <u>blood sugar level</u>, <u>water content</u>, etc.).

# Adrenaline and Thyroxine

On the previous two pages you learnt what <u>hormones</u> are.  Now it's time to look at a <u>couple of examples</u>...

## Adrenaline Prepares You for 'Fight or Flight'

1) <u>Adrenaline</u> is a hormone released by the <u>adrenal glands</u> (which are located just above the kidneys — see page 100).

2) Adrenaline prepares the body for '<u>fight or flight</u>' — in other words, <u>standing</u> your <u>ground</u> in the face of a <u>threat</u> (e.g. a predator) or bravely <u>running away</u>.  It does this by activating processes that increase the supply of <u>oxygen and glucose</u> to cells.  For example:

- Adrenaline <u>binds</u> to specific <u>receptors</u> in the <u>heart</u>.  This causes the heart muscle to <u>contract</u> more frequently and with <u>more force</u>, so heart rate and blood pressure <u>increase</u>.
- This increases <u>blood flow</u> to the <u>muscles</u>, so the cells receive more <u>oxygen</u> and <u>glucose</u> for increased <u>respiration</u>.
- Adrenaline also binds to receptors in the <u>liver</u>.  This causes the liver to <u>break down</u> its <u>glycogen</u> stores (see. p.110) to release <u>glucose</u>.
- This increases the <u>blood glucose level</u>, so there's more glucose in the blood to be transported to the cells.

3) When your brain detects a <u>stressful situation</u>, it sends <u>nervous impulses</u> to the <u>adrenal glands</u>, which respond by secreting <u>adrenaline</u>.  This gets the body ready for <u>action</u>.

## Hormone Release can be Affected by Negative Feedback

Your body can <u>control</u> the levels of hormones (and other substances) in the blood using <u>negative feedback systems</u>.  When the body detects that the level of a substance has gone <u>above or below</u> the <u>normal level</u>, it <u>triggers a response</u> to bring the level <u>back to normal</u> again.  Here's an example of just that:

### Thyroxine Regulates Metabolism

*An underactive thyroid gland can cause weight gain. Less thyroxine is produced, so your metabolic rate drops. This means that less of the glucose you take in gets broken down in respiration, so more is stored as fat.*

1) <u>Thyroxine</u> is a hormone released by the <u>thyroid gland</u>.

2) It plays an important role in regulating <u>metabolic rate</u> — the speed at which chemical reactions in the body occur.

3) A <u>negative feedback system</u> keeps the amount of thyroxine in the blood at the right level:

- When the blood thyroxine level is <u>lower than normal</u>, the <u>hypothalamus</u> (a structure in the brain) is stimulated to release <u>thyrotropin releasing hormone</u> (TRH).
- TRH stimulates the <u>pituitary gland</u> to release <u>thyroid stimulating hormone</u> (TSH).
- TSH stimulates the <u>thyroid gland</u> to release <u>thyroxine</u>, so the blood thyroxine level <u>rises</u> back towards normal.
- When the blood thyroxine level becomes <u>higher than normal</u>, the release of <u>TRH</u> from the hypothalamus is inhibited, which reduces the production of <u>TSH</u>, so the blood thyroxine level <u>falls</u>.

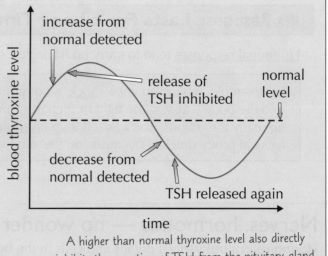

*A higher than normal thyroxine level also directly inhibits the secretion of TSH from the pituitary gland.*

# Warm-Up and Exam Questions

Yep, that's right this topic is no different from the last — there are still plenty of questions for you to get practising what you've learnt. Don't worry, the warm-up questions will ease you in gently.

## Warm-Up Questions

1) What term is used to describe an organ whose cells are affected by a particular hormone?

2) a) Name five endocrine glands found in the male human body.
   b) Name one type of endocrine gland found in the female human body that is not found in the male human body.

3) Name the glands that produce adrenaline.

4) Name the gland that produces thyroxine.

## Exam Questions

1   **Figure 1** shows thyroxine undergoing regulation in the human body.
Changes from the normal thyroxine level trigger a response that returns the level to normal.

(a)   Name the type of system that regulates the level
of a hormone, such as thyroxine, in the blood.

*[1 mark]*

(b)   Which of these things is happening at
point **X** in **Figure 1**?

    ☐   **A**   TRH release is stimulated.

    ☐   **B**   TSH production is increased.

    ☐   **C**   TSH release is inhibited.

    ☐   **D**   Thyroxine release is stimulated.

*[1 mark]*

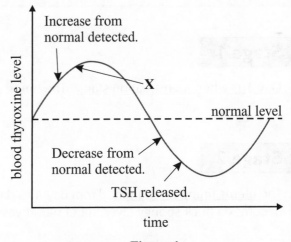

**Figure 1**

2   Hypopituitarism is a condition in which the pituitary gland
doesn't secrete enough of one or more of the pituitary hormones.

People with hypopituitarism may experience tiredness and weight gain.
These symptoms are linked to low thyroid hormone levels.

Suggest why someone with hypopituitarism may experience these symptoms.

*[3 marks]*

3\*   A dog suddenly runs towards a cat across the street, which frightens the cat.

Describe how a hormonal response would affect the cat's heart rate and
blood glucose level when it sees the dog. Explain why these effects are beneficial.

*[6 marks]*

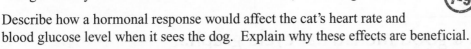

Topic 7 — Animal Coordination, Control and Homeostasis

# The Menstrual Cycle

The monthly <u>release of an egg</u> from a woman's ovaries is part of the <u>menstrual cycle</u>.

## The **Menstrual Cycle** Has **Four Stages**

The menstrual cycle is the <u>monthly sequence of events</u> in which the female body releases an <u>egg</u> and prepares the <u>uterus</u> (womb) in case the egg is <u>fertilised</u>. This is what happens at <u>each stage</u>:

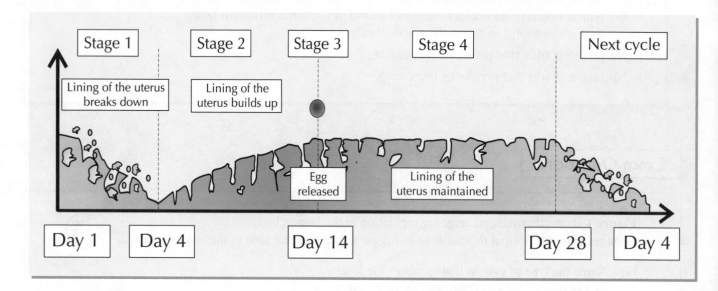

## Stage 1

<u>Day 1 is when menstruation starts</u>. The lining of the uterus breaks down and is released.

*The lining of the uterus is also called the 'endometrium'.*

## Stage 2

<u>The uterus lining is repaired</u>. From day 4 to day 14, the uterus lining builds up again until it becomes a thick spongy layer full of blood vessels, ready for a fertilised egg to implant there.

## Stage 3

<u>An egg develops and is released</u> from the ovary (<u>ovulation</u>) at about day 14.

## Stage 4

<u>The lining is then maintained</u> for about 14 days, until day 28. If no fertilised egg has landed on the uterus wall by day 28, the spongy lining starts to break down again, and the whole cycle starts over.

## Examiners love a good menstrual cycle graph...

Make sure you have a good handle on the different <u>stages</u> of the <u>menstrual cycle</u> before moving on to the next page to learn about the <u>hormones</u> that <u>control</u> those stages — examiners like asking about it.

# The Menstrual Cycle

## The **Menstrual Cycle** is **Controlled** by **Four Hormones**

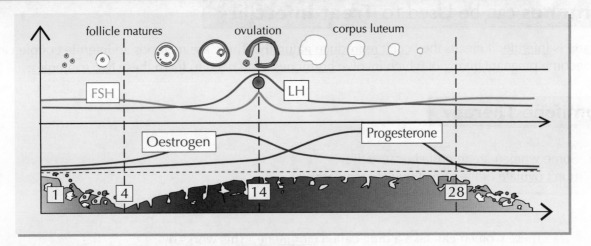

## 1. FSH (Follicle-Stimulating Hormone)

1) Released by the pituitary gland.
2) Causes a follicle (an egg and its surrounding cells) to mature in one of the ovaries.
3) Stimulates oestrogen production.

## 2. Oestrogen

1) Released by the ovaries.
2) Causes the lining of the uterus to thicken and grow.
3) A high level stimulates an LH surge (a rapid increase).

## 3. LH (Luteinising Hormone)

1) Released by the pituitary gland.
2) The LH surge stimulates ovulation at day 14 — the follicle ruptures and the egg is released.
3) Stimulates the remains of the follicle to develop into a structure called a corpus luteum — which secretes progesterone.

## 4. Progesterone

1) Released by the corpus luteum after ovulation.
2) Maintains the lining of the uterus.
3) Inhibits the release of FSH and LH.
4) When the progesterone level falls, and there's a low oestrogen level, the uterus lining breaks down.
5) A low progesterone level allows FSH to increase and then the whole cycle starts again.

If a fertilised egg implants in the uterus (i.e. the woman becomes pregnant) then the level of progesterone will stay high to maintain the lining of the uterus during pregnancy.

# Controlling Fertility

Hormones can be used <u>artificially</u> to help <u>infertile</u> women have babies

## Hormones can be Used to **Treat Infertility**

If a person is <u>infertile</u>, it means they <u>can't reproduce naturally</u>. There are methods an infertile couple can use to become pregnant, many of which involve <u>hormones</u>. You need to learn these <u>two examples</u>:

### Clomifene Therapy

1) Some women are infertile because they <u>don't ovulate</u> or they <u>don't ovulate regularly</u>.

2) These women can take a drug called <u>clomifene</u>. This works by causing more <u>FSH</u> and <u>LH</u> to be released by the body, which <u>stimulates egg maturation and ovulation</u> — see previous page.

3) By knowing when the woman will be ovulating, the couple can have intercourse <u>during this time period</u> to improve the chance of becoming pregnant.

### IVF ("*in vitro* fertilisation")

1) IVF involves collecting <u>eggs</u> from the woman's ovaries and fertilising them in a <u>lab</u> using the man's <u>sperm</u>. These are then grown into <u>embryos</u>.

2) Once the embryos are <u>tiny balls of cells</u>, one or two of them are <u>transferred</u> to the woman's uterus to improve the chance of <u>pregnancy</u>.

3) <u>FSH</u> and <u>LH</u> are given before egg collection to <u>stimulate egg production</u> (so more than one egg can be collected).

4) IVF is an example of <u>Assisted Reproductive Technology</u> (<u>ART</u>) — a fertility treatment that involves eggs being handled (and usually fertilised) <u>outside of the body</u>.

## Understanding how hormones work helps put them to use artificially

Knowing the effects that <u>LH</u> and <u>FSH</u> have on the <u>menstrual cycle</u> allows us the use the hormones to manipulate the menstrual cycle when <u>treating infertility</u>. In <u>clomifene therapy</u> and <u>IVF</u>, FSH and LH are really important because they both <u>stimulate egg production</u>, <u>maturation</u> and <u>ovulation</u>.

# Controlling Fertility

<u>Pregnancy</u> can happen if sperm reaches the ovulated egg.  <u>Contraception</u> tries to <u>stop</u> this happening.

## Contraceptives are Used to **Prevent Pregnancy**

1) <u>Hormones</u> can also be used as <u>contraceptives</u>.  For example, <u>oestrogen</u> can be used to <u>prevent</u> the <u>release</u> of an <u>egg</u>.  This may seem kind of strange (since naturally oestrogen helps stimulate the <u>release</u> of eggs).  But if oestrogen is taken <u>every day</u> to keep the level of it <u>permanently high</u>, it <u>inhibits</u> the production of <u>FSH</u>, and after a while <u>egg development</u> and <u>production stop</u> and stay stopped.

2) <u>Progesterone</u> can also be used to <u>reduce fertility</u>.  It works in several different ways — one of which is by stimulating the production of <u>thick cervical mucus</u>, which <u>prevents</u> any <u>sperm</u> getting through the entrance to the uterus (the <u>cervix</u>) and reaching an egg.

3) Some hormonal contraceptives contain <u>both oestrogen and progesterone</u> — for example, the <u>combined pill</u> (which is an oral contraceptive) and the <u>contraceptive patch</u> (which is worn on the skin).

4) The <u>mini-pill</u> (another oral contraceptive) and the <u>contraceptive injection</u> both contain <u>progesterone only</u>.

5) Pregnancy can also be prevented by <u>barrier methods</u> of contraception — these put a barrier between the <u>sperm</u> and <u>egg</u> so they <u>don't meet</u>.  Examples include <u>condoms</u> (both male and female) and <u>diaphragms</u> (flexible, dome-shaped devices that fit over the opening of the uterus and are inserted before sex).

Diaphragms must be used with a spermicide — a chemical that kills sperm.

## Hormonal and Barrier Contraceptive Methods Have **Pros and Cons**

1) Generally, when <u>used correctly</u>, hormonal methods are <u>more effective</u> at <u>preventing pregnancy</u> than barrier methods.  Also, hormonal methods mean the couple don't have to stop and think about contraception <u>each time</u> they have intercourse (as they would if they relied on barrier methods).

2) However, hormonal methods can have <u>unpleasant side-effects</u>, such as headaches, acne and mood changes.  Also, hormonal methods <u>don't protect</u> against <u>sexually transmitted infections</u> — <u>condoms</u> are the only form of contraception that do this.

**EXAM TIP**

## People have a choice to make when picking a contraceptive

You might be asked to <u>evaluate</u> different <u>methods of contraception</u> in your exam.  If you are, remember: you need to weigh up and write about both the <u>pros</u> and the <u>cons</u> of each method and write a sensible <u>conclusion</u> too.  That's how you get your hands on those top marks.

# Warm-Up and Exam Questions

Right then, another lot of pages down. Now there's just the small matter of answering some questions...

## Warm-Up Questions

1) Name the hormone that stimulates an egg to mature in the ovary.
2) Name the only form of contraception that protects against sexually transmitted infections.
3) What is Assisted Reproductive Technology (ART)?
4) What effect does the drug clomifene have on the release of FSH and LH?

## Exam Questions

**1** The menstrual cycle is controlled by several different hormones.  Grade 4-6

(a) Describe the effect of progesterone on the release of FSH.

*[1 mark]*

(b) Name the hormone responsible for stimulating the formation of the corpus luteum.

*[1 mark]*

(c) State the day of the menstrual cycle on which the egg released.

*[1 mark]*

Towards the end of the menstrual cycle oestrogen, levels are low and progesterone levels begin to fall.

(d) Describe the effect that this will have on the uterus lining.

*[1 mark]*

(e) When a fertilised egg implants in the uterus, the level of progesterone remains high. Suggest why this happens.

*[1 mark]*

**2** A couple are researching which form of contraceptive to use. One option is the combined oral contraceptive pill. The pill contains both oestrogen and progesterone and is taken everyday.  Grade 6-7

(a) Explain how taking oestrogen every day will stop the woman getting pregnant.

*[2 marks]*

(b) State and explain **one** way in which taking a contraceptive pill containing progesterone could stop a woman getting pregnant.

*[2 marks]*

(c) The couple are also considering using barrier contraceptives to prevent pregnancy. Describe how barrier contraceptives prevent pregnancies.

*[1 mark]*

(d) State **one** advantage and **one** disadvantage for the couple if they choose to use a barrier contraceptive instead of a hormonal contraceptive.

*[2 marks]*

# Homeostasis

Homeostasis means maintaining the right conditions inside your body, so that everything works properly. Luckily there are some clever systems in place to keep things plodding along steadily.

## Homeostasis is Maintaining a Constant Internal Environment

1) Conditions in your body need to be kept steady — this is really important because your cells need the right conditions in order to function properly, including the right conditions for enzyme action (see p.27). It can be dangerous for your health if conditions vary too much from normal levels.

2) To maintain a constant internal environment, your body needs to respond to both internal and external changes, whilst balancing inputs (stuff going into your body) with outputs (stuff leaving).

3) Examples of homeostasis in action include:

Blood glucose regulation — you need to make sure the amount of glucose in your blood doesn't get too high or too low (see next page).

Thermoregulation (regulating body temperature) — you need to reduce your body temperature when you're hot, but increase it when the environment is cold.

Osmoregulation (regulating water content) — you need to keep a balance between the water you gain (in drink, food, and from respiration) and the water you pee, sweat and breathe out.

4) Negative feedback systems (see p.102) help to keep conditions in your body steady. This means that if a condition changes away from the normal level, a response is triggered that counteracts the change. E.g. a rise in blood glucose level causes a response that lowers blood glucose level (and vice versa).

## Homeostasis is really important to keep your body "normal"

Without negative feedback systems, changes in your body conditions would go unregulated. This would be really bad because your body wouldn't function properly. So we need homeostasis to keep things in check.

# Blood Glucose Regulation

<u>Insulin</u> and <u>glucagon</u> are <u>hormones</u> that control how much <u>glucose</u> there is in your <u>blood</u>.

## **Insulin** and **Glucagon** Control **Blood Glucose** Concentration

1) Eating foods containing <u>carbohydrate</u> puts <u>glucose</u> into the <u>blood</u> from the <u>small intestine</u>.

2) The normal <u>metabolism</u> of cells <u>removes glucose</u> from the blood.

3) Vigorous <u>exercise</u> removes <u>much more</u> glucose from the blood.

4) <u>Excess</u> glucose can be stored as <u>glycogen</u> in the <u>liver</u> and in the <u>muscles</u>.

5) When these stores are <u>full</u> then the excess glucose is stored as <u>lipid</u> (fat) in the tissues.

6) <u>Changes</u> in blood glucose are monitored and controlled by the <u>pancreas</u>, using the hormones <u>insulin</u> and <u>glucagon</u>, as shown:

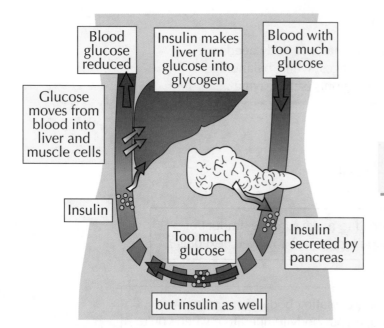

Blood glucose concentration <u>too HIGH — INSULIN</u> is added.

So insulin removes glucose from the blood.

Blood glucose concentration <u>too LOW — GLUCAGON</u> is added.

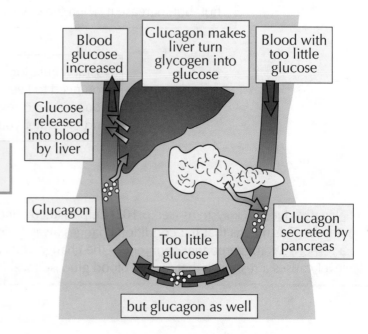

## And people used to think the pancreas was just a cushion...

This stuff can seem a bit confusing at first, but you could have a go at remembering it like this: If blood glucose is <u>increasing</u>, insulin's added.  If blood glucose is almost <u>gone</u>, glucagon's added.

# Diabetes

Diabetes is an example of when homeostasis <u>doesn't work</u>. Make sure you fully understand how <u>insulin</u> affects <u>blood glucose concentration</u> (on the previous page) before you try getting your head around diabetes.

## Type 1 Diabetes — Caused by a **Lack of Insulin**

1) <u>Type 1 diabetes</u> is a condition where the <u>pancreas produces little or no insulin</u>. The result is that a person's blood glucose can <u>rise</u> to a level that can <u>kill them</u>.

*Remember, insulin reduces blood glucose level.*

2) A person with type 1 diabetes will need to be <u>treated</u> with <u>insulin therapy</u> — this usually involves <u>injecting insulin</u> into the blood. This is often done at mealtimes to make sure that the <u>glucose</u> is removed from the blood <u>quickly</u> once the food has been <u>digested</u>. This stops the level of glucose in the blood from getting too high and is a <u>very effective treatment</u>. Insulin is usually injected into <u>subcutaneous tissue</u> (fatty tissue just under the skin). The <u>amount of insulin</u> that needs to be injected depends on the person's <u>diet</u> and how <u>active</u> they are.

3) As well as insulin therapy, people with type 1 diabetes also need to think about:

*Injecting too much insulin could result in a dangerously low blood glucose level.*

- <u>Limiting their intake</u> of foods rich in simple carbohydrates, i.e. sugars (which cause the blood glucose level to rise rapidly).
- Taking <u>regular exercise</u> — this helps to <u>remove excess glucose</u> from the blood.

## Type 2 Diabetes — a Person is **Resistant to Insulin**

1) <u>Type 2 diabetes</u> is a condition where the <u>pancreas doesn't produce enough insulin</u> or when a person becomes <u>resistant to insulin</u> (their body's cells <u>don't respond</u> properly to the hormone). In both of these cases, blood glucose level <u>rises</u>.

2) There is a <u>correlation</u> (see p.14) between <u>obesity</u> and <u>type 2 diabetes</u> — this means that obese people have an <u>increased risk</u> of developing type 2 diabetes. People are classified as <u>obese</u> if they have a <u>body mass index</u> (BMI) of <u>over 30</u>. BMI is worked out using this formula:

$$\text{BMI} = \frac{\text{mass (kg)}}{(\text{height (m)})^2}$$

*See page 85 for more on calculating BMI and waist-to-hip ratios.*

3) Where the body <u>stores excess fat</u> is also important — storing a lot of fat around the <u>abdomen</u> (tummy area) is associated with an <u>increased risk</u> of developing type 2 diabetes. Calculating a person's <u>waist-to-hip ratio</u> gives an indication of how fat is stored. This is the formula you need:

$$\text{Waist-to-hip ratio} = \frac{\text{waist circumference (cm)}}{\text{hip circumference (cm)}}$$

4) A ratio above <u>1.0 for men</u> and above <u>0.85 for women</u> is associated with an increased risk of type 2 diabetes because it indicates that a lot of fat is being stored around the abdomen.

5) Type 2 diabetes can be <u>controlled</u> by eating a <u>healthy diet</u>, getting regular <u>exercise</u> and <u>losing weight</u> if needed. Some people with type 2 diabetes also have <u>medication</u> or <u>insulin injections</u>.

# Warm-Up and Exam Questions

Welcome to some more questions. There are quite a few of them, but that's because they're pretty important.

## Warm-Up Questions

1) What is homeostasis?
2) What does insulin do?
3) What is Type 2 diabetes?
4) Name one factor that increases your risk of developing Type 2 diabetes.

## Exam Questions

1   **Figure 1** shows how the blood glucose level is regulated in humans.

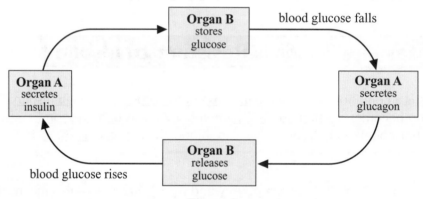

**Figure 1**

(a)   What are the names of organs **A** and **B** in **Figure 1**?

| | | Organ A | Organ B |
|---|---|---|---|
| ☐ | A | pancreas | kidney |
| ☐ | B | liver | pancreas |
| ☐ | C | kidney | liver |
| ☐ | D | pancreas | liver |

*[1 mark]*

(b)   Apart from organ **B** releasing glucose, suggest **one** reason why a person's blood glucose level might rise.

*[1 mark]*

(c)   With reference to **Figure 1**, explain what goes wrong with the regulation of blood glucose level in people with Type 1 diabetes.

*[3 marks]*

(d)   Describe what the hormone glucagon does.

*[1 mark]*

# Revision Summary for Topic 7

Yay, you've made it to the end of <u>Topic 7</u> — now for some questions to make sure you've been paying attention...

Try these questions and <u>tick off each one</u> when you <u>get it right</u>.

When you've done <u>all the questions</u> under a heading and are <u>completely happy</u>, tick it off.

## Hormones (p.100-102) ☑

1) What is a hormone? ☑

2) How do hormones travel to target organs? ☑

3) What is an endocrine gland? ☑

4) Name the gland where each of the following hormones is produced:
   a) oestrogen,   b) testosterone,   c) insulin. ☑

5) Which hormone prepares the body for the 'fight or flight' response? ☑

6) Describe how a negative feedback system works in the body. ☑

7) Which hormone, released by the thyroid gland, controls metabolic rate? ☑

## The Menstrual Cycle and Fertility (p.104-107) ☐

8) Draw and label a timeline of the 28 day menstrual cycle. ☑

9) Describe two effects of FSH on the body. ☑

10) Describe two effects of oestrogen on the body. ☑

11) Which hormone is secreted by a corpus luteum? ☑

12) What is clomifene therapy?  Who might use it? ☑

13) Briefly describe how IVF is carried out. ☑

14) Write down two pros and two cons of hormonal contraceptives. ☑

## Homeostasis (p.109-111) ☐

15) Name the two hormones that are involved in controlling
    blood glucose concentration in the human body. ☑

16) Explain how type 1 and type 2 diabetes can be treated. ☑

# Exchange of Materials

Like all organisms, animals need to exchange things with their environment — but being multicellular makes things a little bit complicated...

## Organisms Exchange Substances with their Environment

1) All organisms must take in substances that they need from the environment and get rid of any waste products. For example:

> Cells need oxygen for aerobic respiration (see page 116), which produces carbon dioxide as a waste product. These two gases move between cells and the environment by diffusion (see next page).

> Water is taken up by cells by osmosis. In animals, dissolved food molecules (the products of digestion, e.g. glucose, amino acids) and mineral ions diffuse along with it.

> Urea (a waste product produced by animals from proteins) diffuses from cells to the blood plasma for removal from the body by the kidneys.

*There's more on diffusion and osmosis on pages 32-33.*

2) How easy it is for an organism to exchange substances with its environment depends on the organism's surface area to volume ratio (SA : V).

## You Can Compare Surface Area to Volume Ratios

A ratio shows how big one value is compared to another. The larger an organism is, the smaller its surface area is compared to its volume. You can show this by calculating surface area to volume ratios:

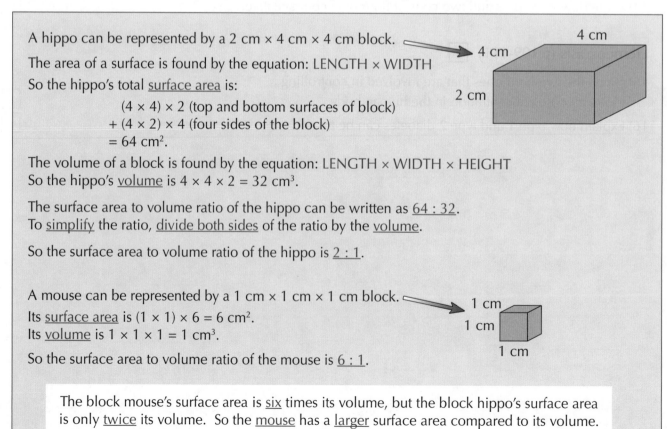

A hippo can be represented by a 2 cm × 4 cm × 4 cm block.

The area of a surface is found by the equation: LENGTH × WIDTH

So the hippo's total surface area is:

$\qquad$ (4 × 4) × 2 (top and bottom surfaces of block)
$\qquad$ + (4 × 2) × 4 (four sides of the block)
$\qquad$ = 64 cm².

The volume of a block is found by the equation: LENGTH × WIDTH × HEIGHT
So the hippo's volume is 4 × 4 × 2 = 32 cm³.

The surface area to volume ratio of the hippo can be written as 64 : 32.
To simplify the ratio, divide both sides of the ratio by the volume.

So the surface area to volume ratio of the hippo is 2 : 1.

A mouse can be represented by a 1 cm × 1 cm × 1 cm block.
Its surface area is (1 × 1) × 6 = 6 cm².
Its volume is 1 × 1 × 1 = 1 cm³.
So the surface area to volume ratio of the mouse is 6 : 1.

> The block mouse's surface area is six times its volume, but the block hippo's surface area is only twice its volume. So the mouse has a larger surface area compared to its volume.

# Exchange Surfaces and the Alveoli

The alveoli are an <u>exchange surface</u> found in the lungs of mammals. They're <u>well-adapted</u> for the <u>efficient exchange</u> of two important <u>gases</u> — oxygen and carbon dioxide.

## Multicellular Organisms Need Exchange Surfaces

1) In <u>single-celled organisms</u>, gases and dissolved substances can diffuse <u>directly into</u> (or out of) the cell across the cell membrane — it's because they have a <u>large surface area</u> compared to their <u>volume</u>, so <u>enough substances</u> can be exchanged across the membrane to supply the volume of the cell.

2) <u>Multicellular organisms</u> (such as <u>animals</u>) have a <u>smaller surface area</u> compared to their <u>volume</u>. This makes it difficult to exchange <u>enough substances</u> to supply their <u>entire volume</u> across their <u>outside surface</u> alone. So they need some sort of <u>exchange surface</u> for efficient diffusion and a <u>mass transport system</u> to move substances between the exchange surface and the rest of the body.

3) The exchange surfaces have to allow <u>enough</u> of the necessary substances to pass through, so they are <u>adapted</u> to maximise effectiveness.

## Gas Exchange in Mammals Happens in the Alveoli

1) The job of the lungs is to transfer <u>oxygen</u> ($O_2$) to the <u>blood</u> and to <u>remove</u> waste <u>carbon dioxide</u> ($CO_2$) from it.

2) To do this, the lungs contain millions of little air sacs called <u>alveoli</u> where <u>gas exchange</u> takes place.

3) Blood <u>arriving</u> at the alveoli has just returned to the lungs from the <u>rest of the body</u>, so it contains <u>lots of $CO_2$</u> and <u>not much $O_2$</u>. This maximises the <u>concentration gradient</u> for the diffusion of both gases.

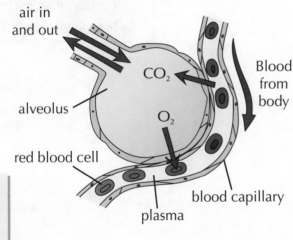

air in and out

$CO_2$

$O_2$

alveolus

red blood cell

plasma

blood capillary

Blood from body

*Remember — one alveolus, many alveoli.*

4) $O_2$ <u>diffuses out</u> of the <u>air</u> in the <u>alveoli</u> (where the concentration of $O_2$ is <u>high</u>) and into the <u>blood</u> (where the concentration of $O_2$ is <u>low</u>). $CO_2$ diffuses in the <u>opposite direction</u> to be breathed out.

5) The alveoli are specialised to maximise the <u>diffusion</u> of $O_2$ and $CO_2$. They have:
   - A moist lining for <u>dissolving</u> gases.
   - A good <u>blood supply</u> to maintain the concentration gradients of $O_2$ and $CO_2$.
   - <u>Very thin</u> walls — minimising the <u>distance</u> that gases have to move.
   - An enormous <u>surface area</u> (about 75 m² in humans).

$O_2$ and $CO_2$ diffuse across the membranes of the cells that make up the walls of the capillary and alveolus. These membranes are partially permeable — see page 33.

## Humans need alveoli for gas exchange...

You might well get asked to explain how the <u>adaptations</u> of the alveoli help gas exchange, so make sure you know what those adaptations are and why they maximise the diffusion of $O_2$ and $CO_2$.

# Respiration

You need <u>energy</u> to keep your body going. Energy comes from <u>food</u>, and it's <u>released</u> by <u>respiration</u>.

## Cellular Respiration Releases Energy

1) Respiration is <u>NOT</u> breathing in and breathing out.

2) <u>Respiration</u> actually goes on in <u>every cell</u> of all living organisms — and it happens <u>continuously</u>.

3) It's the process of <u>transferring</u> (releasing) <u>energy</u> from the breakdown of <u>organic compounds</u> (usually <u>glucose</u>). The <u>energy</u> is then used for things like:

Organic compounds are compounds containing carbon. They include carbohydrates, lipids and proteins.

- <u>metabolic processes</u> — such as making larger molecules from smaller ones (e.g. proteins from amino acids),
- <u>contracting muscles</u> (in animals),
- <u>maintaining</u> a steady <u>body temperature</u> (in mammals and birds).

4) Because energy is transferred <u>to the environment</u>, respiration is an <u>exothermic reaction</u>. Some of this energy is transferred by <u>heating</u>.

5) There are <u>two types</u> of respiration, <u>aerobic</u> and <u>anaerobic</u>.

## Aerobic Respiration Needs Plenty of Oxygen

1) <u>Aerobic respiration</u> is what happens when there's <u>plenty of oxygen</u> available.

2) <u>Aerobic</u> just means "<u>with oxygen</u>" and it's the most efficient way to transfer <u>energy</u> from <u>glucose</u>.

3) This type of respiration goes on <u>all the time</u> in <u>plants</u> and <u>animals</u>. Here's the <u>equation</u>:

$$\text{glucose} + \text{oxygen} \longrightarrow \text{carbon dioxide} + \text{water}$$

$$C_6H_{12}O_6 + 6O_2 \longrightarrow 6CO_2 + 6H_2O$$

This is the reverse of the photosynthesis equation (see page 90).

# Respiration

## Anaerobic Respiration Doesn't Use Oxygen At All

1) When you do really <u>vigorous exercise</u> your body can't supply enough <u>oxygen</u> to your muscles for aerobic respiration — even though your <u>heart rate</u> and <u>breathing rate</u> increase as much as they can. Your muscles have to start <u>respiring anaerobically</u> as well.

2) <u>Anaerobic</u> just means "<u>without</u> oxygen". It transfers much <u>less energy</u> than aerobic respiration so it's much less <u>efficient</u>. In anaerobic respiration, the glucose is only <u>partially</u> broken down, and <u>lactic acid</u> is also produced.

3) The <u>lactic acid</u> builds up in the muscles — it gets <u>painful</u> and leads to <u>cramp</u>.

4) This is the <u>word equation</u> for anaerobic respiration in <u>animals</u>:

$$glucose \longrightarrow lactic\ acid$$

## Anaerobic Respiration in Plants is Slightly Different

1) <u>Plants</u> can respire <u>without oxygen</u> too, but they produce <u>ethanol</u> (alcohol) and $CO_2$ <u>instead</u> of lactic acid.

2) This is the <u>word equation</u> for anaerobic respiration in <u>plants</u>:

Fungi such as yeast also do anaerobic respiration like this.

$$glucose \longrightarrow ethanol + carbon\ dioxide$$

## Respiration releases energy from glucose

You need to be able to compare <u>anaerobic</u> and <u>aerobic</u> respiration for your exam. Remember, anaerobic respiration has <u>different products</u> to aerobic respiration and transfers much <u>less energy</u>, as well as taking place <u>without oxygen</u>. Both aerobic and anaerobic respiration are <u>exothermic</u> though — don't forget that.

# Investigating Respiration

The rate at which an organism respires will change depending on different factors. You can do experiments to see how these factors affect the rate of respiration.

## You Can Measure the Rate of Respiration Using a Respirometer

In aerobic respiration, organisms use up oxygen from the air. By measuring the amount of oxygen consumed by organisms in a given time, you can calculate their rate of respiration.

Here's an experiment which uses woodlice, a water bath and a piece of equipment called a respirometer. It allows you to measure the effect of temperature on the rate of respiration of the woodlice. (You could use germinating peas or beans instead of woodlice. Germinating seeds respire to provide energy for growth.)

1) Some soda lime granules are added to two test tubes. The soda lime absorbs the $CO_2$ produced by the respiring woodlice in the experiment. (You could use cotton wool soaked in a few drops of potassium hydroxide solution to absorb the $CO_2$ produced by the woodlice instead.)

   *Soda lime is corrosive. Safety goggles and gloves are worn when handling it to protect the eyes and skin.*

2) A ball of cotton wool is placed above the soda lime in each tube. Woodlice are placed on top of the cotton wool in one tube. Glass beads with the same mass as the woodlice are used in the control tube. (There's more on controls on page 6.)

3) The respirometer is then set up as shown in the diagram.

4) The syringe is used to set the fluid in the manometer to a known level.

5) The apparatus is then left for a set period of time in a water bath set to 15 °C.

6) During this time, there'll be a decrease in the volume of the air in the test tube containing the woodlice. This is because the woodlice use up oxygen in the tube as they respire. (The $CO_2$ they produce is absorbed by the soda lime so it doesn't affect the experiment.)

*Diagram labels: syringe, calibrated scale, manometer containing coloured fluid, closed tap, live woodlice on cotton wool, soda lime granules, water bath, test tube, glass beads, control tube*

7) The decrease in volume reduces the pressure in the tube, causing the coloured liquid in the manometer to move towards the test tube containing the woodlice.

8) The distance moved by the liquid in a given time is measured. From this you can calculate the volume of oxygen taken in by the woodlice per minute — this is the rate of respiration in, e.g. $cm^3 min^{-1}$.

9) Repeat steps 1-8 with the water bath set at different temperatures, e.g. 20 °C and 25 °C. This will allow you to see how changing the temperature affects the rate of respiration.

Any live animals you use in this experiment should be treated ethically (e.g. it's important not to leave woodlice in a respirometer for too long, or they may run out of oxygen and die). There's more about treating organisms ethically on page 144.

*You should make sure that the woodlice can't come into contact with the soda lime too.*

Topic 8 — Exchange and Transport in Animals

# Warm-Up and Exam Questions

There's no better way to practice exam questions than doing... err... practice exam questions.
Hang on, what's this I see...

## Warm-Up Questions

1) Give two examples of how animals use the energy transferred by respiration.
2) Name two substances that diffuse out from cells into the bloodstream.
3) What are the reactants of aerobic respiration?
4) Name a piece of scientific equipment that can be used to measure the rate of respiration in living organisms.

## Exam Questions

1   The lungs contain millions of air sacs, called alveoli, which are adapted   **Grade 4-6**
    for the efficient exchange of oxygen and carbon dioxide in respiration.

(a)   Which of the following is a correct description of the diffusion of oxygen in gas exchange?

☐ **A**   Oxygen diffuses out of the blood, where the concentration of oxygen is high, into the alveoli, where the concentration of oxygen is low.

☐ **B**   Oxygen diffuses out of the blood, where the concentration of oxygen is low, into the alveoli, where the concentration of oxygen is high

☐ **C**   Oxygen diffuses out of the air in the alveoli, where the concentration of oxygen is high, into the blood, where the concentration of oxygen is low.

☐ **D**   Oxygen diffuses out of the air in the alveoli, where the concentration of oxygen is low, into the blood, where the concentration of oxygen is high.

*[1 mark]*

(b)   Describe how the thickness of the alveoli walls improves the efficiency of gas exchange in the lungs.

*[2 marks]*

2   Respiration is a process carried out by all living cells.   **Grade 4-6**
    It can take place aerobically or anaerobically.

(a)   State the purpose of respiration.

*[1 mark]*

(b)   Give **two** differences between aerobic and anaerobic respiration.

*[2 marks]*

(c)   Write the word equation for anaerobic respiration in humans.

*[2 marks]*

3   A bacterial cell can be represented by a 2 μm × 2 μm × 1 μm block.   **Grade 7-9**
    Calculate the cell's surface area to volume ratio.

*[3 marks]*

# Circulatory System — Blood

Blood is a tissue. One of its jobs is to act as a huge transport system. There are four main things in blood...

## Red Blood Cells Carry Oxygen

1) The job of red blood cells (also called erythrocytes) is to carry oxygen from the lungs to all the cells in the body.

The more red blood cells you've got, the more oxygen can get to your cells. At high altitudes there's less oxygen in the air — so people who live there produce more red blood cells to compensate.

2) They have a biconcave disc shape (in other words, they look a bit like a jam doughnut that's being pressed in at the top and bottom) to give a large surface area for absorbing oxygen.

3) They don't have a nucleus — this allows more room to carry oxygen.

4) They contain a red pigment called haemoglobin, which contains iron.

5) In the lungs, haemoglobin binds to oxygen to become oxyhaemoglobin. In body tissues, the reverse happens — oxyhaemoglobin splits up into haemoglobin and oxygen, to release oxygen to the cells.

## White Blood Cells Defend Against Infection

Unlike red blood cells, white blood cells do have a nucleus.

1) Phagocytes are white blood cells that can change shape to engulf (gobble up) unwelcome microorganisms — this is called phagocytosis.

2) Lymphocytes are white blood cells that produce antibodies against microorganisms (see p.78). Some also produce antitoxins to neutralise any toxins produced by the microorganisms.

3) When you have an infection, your white blood cells multiply to fight it off — so a blood test will show a high white blood cell count.

# Circulatory System — Blood

## Platelets Help Blood Clot

1) These are small fragments of cells. They have no nucleus.

2) They help the blood to clot at a wound — to stop all your blood pouring out and to stop microorganisms getting in. (So platelets basically float about waiting for accidents to happen.)

3) Lack of platelets can cause excessive bleeding and bruising.

## Plasma is the Liquid That Carries Everything in Blood

This is a pale, straw-coloured liquid which carries just about everything:

1) Red and white blood cells and platelets.

2) Nutrients like glucose and amino acids. These are the soluble products of digestion which are absorbed from the gut and taken to the cells of the body.

3) Carbon dioxide from the organs to the lungs.

4) Urea, from the liver to the kidneys.

5) Hormones.

6) Proteins.

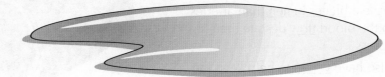

7) Antibodies and antitoxins produced by the white blood cells.

# Circulatory System — Blood Vessels

<u>Blood</u> needs a good set of 'tubes' to carry it round the body.  Here's a page on the different types:

## Blood Vessels are Designed for Their Function

There are <u>three</u> different types of <u>blood vessel</u>:

1) <u>ARTERIES</u> — these carry the blood <u>away</u> from the heart.

2) <u>CAPILLARIES</u> — these are involved in the <u>exchange of materials</u> at the tissues.

3) <u>VEINS</u> — these carry the blood <u>to</u> the heart.

## Arteries Carry Blood Under Pressure

1) The heart pumps the blood out at <u>high pressure</u> so the artery walls are <u>strong</u> and <u>elastic</u>.

2) The walls are <u>thick</u> compared to the size of the hole down the middle (the "<u>lumen</u>").

3) They contain thick layers of <u>muscle</u> to make them <u>strong</u>, and <u>elastic fibres</u> to allow them to stretch and <u>spring back</u>.

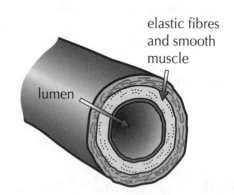

elastic fibres and smooth muscle

lumen

## Capillaries are Really Small

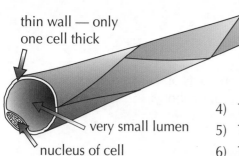

thin wall — only one cell thick

very small lumen

nucleus of cell

1) Arteries branch into <u>capillaries</u>.

2) Capillaries are really <u>tiny</u> — too small to see.

3) They are very <u>narrow</u>, so they can squeeze into the gaps between cells.  This means they can carry the blood <u>really close</u> to <u>every cell</u> in the body to <u>exchange substances</u> with them.

4) They have <u>permeable</u> walls, so substances can <u>diffuse</u> in and out.

5) They supply <u>food</u> and <u>oxygen</u>, and take away <u>waste</u> like $CO_2$.

6) Their walls are usually <u>only one cell thick</u>.  This <u>increases</u> the rate of diffusion by <u>decreasing</u> the <u>distance</u> over which it occurs.

## Veins Take Blood Back to the Heart

1) Capillaries eventually <u>join up</u> to form <u>veins</u>.

2) The blood is at <u>lower pressure</u> in the veins so the walls don't need to be as <u>thick</u> as artery walls.

3) They have a <u>bigger lumen</u> than arteries to help the blood <u>flow</u> despite the lower pressure.

4) They also have <u>valves</u> to help keep the blood flowing in the <u>right direction</u>.

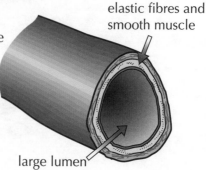

elastic fibres and smooth muscle

large lumen

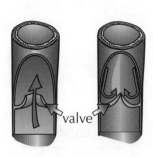

valve

---

### Blood vessels carry blood around the body...

It's easy to forget which vessels carry blood where.  Remember, <u>a</u>rteries carry the blood <u>a</u>way from the heart, ve<u>in</u>s carry the blood back <u>in</u>to the heart and <u>c</u>apillaries carry blood <u>c</u>lose to <u>c</u>ells.

# Circulatory System — The Heart

The <u>heart</u> plays a major role in the circulatory system. It is needed to <u>pump the blood</u> through the blood vessels so that material can be <u>transported</u> to and from the cells.

## Mammals Have a Double Circulatory System

1) This means that the heart pumps blood around the body in <u>two circuits</u>.

> In the first circuit, the heart pumps <u>deoxygenated blood</u> to the <u>lungs</u> to <u>take in oxygen</u>. Oxygenated blood then returns to the heart.

> In the <u>second circuit</u>, the heart pumps <u>oxygenated blood</u> around all the <u>other organs</u> of the body to deliver oxygen to the body cells. Deoxygenated blood then returns to the heart.

2) <u>Fish</u> have a <u>single circulatory system</u> — deoxygenated blood from the fish's body travels to the heart, which then pumps it <u>right round</u> the body again in a <u>single circuit</u> (via the gills where it picks up oxygen).

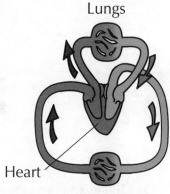

Lungs

Heart

Rest of Body

## The Heart Pumps Blood Through the Blood Vessels

The mammalian heart has <u>four chambers</u> and <u>four major blood vessels</u>. *A fish's heart only has two chambers.*

1) The <u>right atrium</u> of the heart receives <u>deoxygenated</u> blood from the <u>body</u> (through the <u>vena cava</u>).

2) The deoxygenated blood moves through to the <u>right ventricle</u>, which pumps it to the <u>lungs</u> (via the <u>pulmonary artery</u>).

3) The <u>left atrium</u> receives <u>oxygenated</u> blood from the <u>lungs</u> (through the <u>pulmonary vein</u>).

4) The oxygenated blood then moves through to the <u>left ventricle</u>, which pumps it out round the <u>whole body</u> (via the <u>aorta</u>).

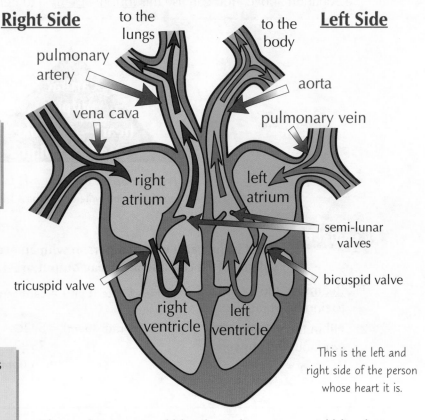

**Right Side** — to the lungs — to the body — **Left Side**

pulmonary artery

vena cava

aorta

pulmonary vein

right atrium

left atrium

semi-lunar valves

tricuspid valve

bicuspid valve

right ventricle

left ventricle

*This is the left and right side of the person whose heart it is.*

Blue = deoxygenated blood. Red = oxygenated blood.

The <u>left</u> ventricle has a much <u>thicker wall</u> than the <u>right</u> ventricle. It needs more <u>muscle</u> because it has to pump blood around the <u>whole body</u> at high pressure, whereas the right ventricle only has to pump it to the <u>lungs</u>. <u>Valves</u> prevent the <u>backflow</u> of blood in the heart.

# Circulatory System — The Heart

## You Can Calculate **How Much** Blood is Pumped **Every Minute**

1) Cardiac output is the total volume of blood pumped by a ventricle every minute.

2) You can calculate it using this equation:

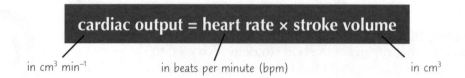

**cardiac output = heart rate × stroke volume**

in cm³ min⁻¹        in beats per minute (bpm)        in cm³

3) The heart rate is the number of beats per minute (bpm).

4) The stroke volume is the volume of blood pumped by one ventricle each time it contracts.

5) You might be asked to find the stroke volume or the heart rate in the exam instead of the cardiac output — if so, you can just rearrange the equation above. You can use this formula triangle to help you:

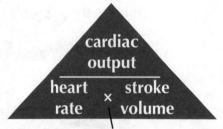

$$\dfrac{\text{cardiac output}}{\text{heart rate} \quad \times \quad \text{stroke volume}}$$

Just cover up the thing you want to find with
your finger and write down what's left showing.

**EXAMPLE:**  **What is the heart rate of a person with an average stroke volume of 72 cm³ and a cardiac output of 5420 cm³ min⁻¹?**

1) Rearrange the formula to find heart rate.

Heart rate (bpm) = cardiac output (cm³ min⁻¹) ÷ stroke volume (cm³)

2) Fill in the values and work out the answer.

Heart rate (bpm) = 5420 ÷ 72
= 75.27...
= 75 bpm (2 s.f.)

For more on rounding to
significant figures, see page 9.

---

**MATHS TIP**

## Make sure you learn the equation...

If you're struggling to remember the equation, think it through logically — if you know
the volume of blood pumped during each ventricle contraction (stroke volume),
and how many contractions there are a minute (heart rate), you can multiply them
to find the total volume of blood pumped each minute (cardiac output).

# Warm-Up and Exam Questions

Who knew the circulatory system had so many different parts, with so many different functions?
Time to check you remember them all...

## Warm-Up Questions

1) What do veins do?
2) Describe the purpose of platelets in blood.
3) Give three things that are carried in blood plasma.
4) Give the equation for calculating cardiac output.

## Exam Questions

1   Blood is a tissue which transports important components, such as red blood cells, around the body.

   (a)   Name the other main type of blood cell, and state its function.

   *[2 marks]*

   (b)   Blood cells are carried in the bloodstream inside blood vessels.
         Capillaries are one type of blood vessel.

         State and explain **two** ways that the structure of a capillary enables it to carry out its function.

   *[4 marks]*

2   **Figure 1** shows the human heart and four blood vessels, as seen from the front.
    The left ventricle has been labelled.

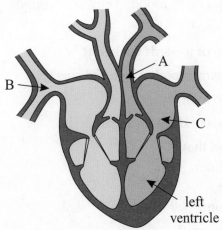

**Figure 1**

   (a)   Name the parts labelled A, B and C.

   *[1 mark]*

   (b)   Describe the function of the left ventricle.

   *[1 mark]*

   (c)   Give the function of the valves in the heart.

   *[1 mark]*

   (d)   Describe the passage of deoxygenated blood from the body through the heart to reach the lungs.

   *[4 marks]*

# Revision Summary for Topic 8

So that's <u>Topic 8</u> — lots of information about exchange and transport in animals.  Time to test yourself...

*   Try these questions and <u>tick off each one</u> when you <u>get it right</u>.
*   When you've done <u>all the questions</u> under a heading and are <u>completely happy</u>, tick it off.

## Exchange of Materials and the Alveoli (p.114-115)  ☑

1)   Name three substances that animals have to exchange with their environment.  ☑
2)   Why do multicellular organisms need specialised exchange surfaces?  ☑
3)   Why do multicellular organisms need mass transport systems?  ☑
4)   Where does gas exchange take place within the lungs?  ☑
5)   Explain the movement of oxygen between the alveoli and the blood.  ☑

## Respiration (p.116-118)  ☑

6)   Is respiration exothermic or endothermic?  Explain your answer.  ☑
7)   What are the products of aerobic respiration?  ☑
8)   Under what circumstances do muscles perform anaerobic respiration?  ☑
9)   When using a respirometer to measure the oxygen consumption of respiring organisms, what is the purpose of the soda lime in the respirometer?  ☑

## The Circulatory System (p.120-124)  ☑

10) Describe the shape of an erythrocyte.  ☑
11) What is the name of the pigment contained within red blood cells and what does it do?  ☑
12) What is the function of lymphocytes?  ☑
13) Name the component of blood that helps blood to clot at a wound.  ☑
14) What is the function of blood plasma?  ☑
15) Do arteries carry blood away from or towards the heart?  ☑
16) How are arteries adapted for carrying blood at high pressure?  ☑
17) Why are the walls of capillaries so thin?  ☑
18) What is the function of the valves found within veins?  ☑
19) Write the name of the blood vessel that:
    a)   carries blood into the right atrium.
    b)   carries blood towards the lungs.
    c)   carries blood into the left atrium.  ☑
20) What is the equation for cardiac output?  ☑
21) How would you calculate the heart rate of an individual if you were given values for their cardiac output and stroke volume?  ☑

# Ecosystems and Interactions Between Organisms

Organisms live together in ecosystems. They depend on other organisms in their ecosystem for survival.

## Ecosystems are Organised into Different Levels

Ecosystems have different levels of organisation:

| Level | Definition |
|---|---|
| Individual | A single organism. |
| Population | All the organisms of one species in a habitat. |
| Community | All the organisms of different species living in a habitat. |
| Ecosystem | A community of organisms along with all the non-living (abiotic) conditions (see next page). |

*A habitat is the place where an organism lives, e.g. a rocky shore or a field.*

*A species is a group of similar organisms that can reproduce to give fertile offspring.*

## Organisms in a Community Are Interdependent

1) Organisms depend on each other for things like food and shelter in order to survive and reproduce. This is known as interdependence. It means that a change in the population of one species can have huge knock on effects for other species in the same community.

2) Mutualism is a relationship between two organisms, from which both organisms benefit. E.g. bees and flowering plants have a mutualistic relationship. When bees visit flowers to get nectar, pollen is transferred to their bodies. The bees then spread the pollen to other plants when they land on their flowers. The bees get food and the plants get help reproducing. Everyone's a winner.

3) Parasites live very closely with a host species (e.g. in or on them). The parasite takes what it needs to survive, but the host doesn't benefit. E.g. fleas are parasites of mammals such as dogs. Fleas feed on their host's blood, but don't offer anything in return.

## Interdependence is the key to communities

Because all organisms in a community share the same habitat, different species are often dependent on each other. Some species rely on each other so much that one couldn't survive without the other.

# Ecosystems and Interactions Between Organisms

The environment in which organisms live <u>changes</u> all the time.  The things that change are either <u>abiotic</u> (non-living) or <u>biotic</u> (living) factors.  These can have a big <u>effect</u> on a community...

## Environmental Changes **Affect Communities** in **Different Ways**

The <u>environment</u> in which plants and animals live <u>changes all the time</u>.  These changes are caused by <u>abiotic</u> (non-living) and <u>biotic</u> (living) factors.  They will affect communities in different ways — for some species <u>population size</u> may <u>increase</u>, for others it may <u>decrease</u>, or the <u>distribution</u> of populations (where they live) may change.  Here are some <u>examples</u> of the effects of changes in <u>abiotic</u> and <u>biotic</u> factors:

### Abiotic Factors Affect Communities...

#### Temperature

E.g. the distribution of <u>bird species</u> in Germany is probably changing because of a rise in average temperature.  For instance, the <u>European Bee-Eater bird</u> is a <u>Mediterranean</u> species but it's now present in parts of <u>Germany</u>.

#### Amount of Water

E.g. <u>daisies</u> grow best in soils that are <u>slightly damp</u>.  If the soil becomes <u>waterlogged</u> or <u>too dry</u>, the population of daisies will <u>decrease</u>.

#### Light Intensity

E.g. as trees grow and provide more <u>shade</u>, <u>grasses</u> may be replaced by <u>fungi</u> (or <u>mosses</u>, etc.) which are better able to <u>cope</u> with the <u>lower light intensity</u>.

#### Levels of pollutants

E.g. <u>lichen</u> are unable to survive if the concentration of <u>sulfur dioxide</u> (an <u>air pollutant</u>) is too <u>high</u>.

### ...and so do **Biotic** Factors

#### Competition

Organisms <u>compete with other species</u> (and members of their own species) for the <u>same resources</u>.  E.g. red and grey <u>squirrels</u> live in the same habitat and eat the same food.  Competition with the grey squirrels for these resources in some areas means there's not enough food for the reds — the <u>population</u> of red squirrels is <u>decreasing</u>, partly as a result of this.

#### Predation

E.g. if the <u>number of lions</u> (predators) <u>decreases</u> then the number of <u>gazelles</u> (their prey) might <u>increase</u> because <u>fewer</u> of them will be <u>eaten</u> by the lions.

# Investigating Ecosystems

This is where the <u>fun</u> starts. Studying <u>ecosystems</u> gives you the chance to <u>rummage around</u> in bushes, get your hands <u>dirty</u> and look at some <u>real organisms</u>, living in the <u>wild</u>.

## Use **Quadrats** to **Study** the **Distribution of Small Organisms**

A <u>quadrat</u> is a <u>square</u> frame enclosing a <u>known area</u>, e.g. 1 m². To compare <u>how common</u> an organism is in <u>two sample areas</u> just follow these simple steps:

1) Place a <u>1 m² quadrat</u> on the ground at a <u>random point</u> within the <u>first</u> sample area. You could do this by dividing the sample area into a grid and using a random number generator to pick coordinates to place your quadrats at. This will help to make sure the results you get are representative of the whole sample area.

2) <u>Count</u> all the organisms you're interested in <u>within</u> the quadrat.

3) <u>Repeat</u> steps 1 and 2 lots of times.

4) <u>Work out</u> the <u>mean</u> number of organisms per quadrat within the first sample area — this is the <u>total number of organisms</u> you counted <u>divided by</u> the <u>number of quadrats</u> you placed.

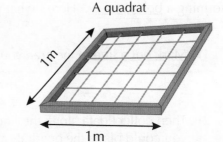

A quadrat

1m

1m

**Anna counted the number of daisies in 7 quadrats that she placed at random in her first sample area. She recorded the following results: 18, 20, 22, 23, 23, 23, 25.**

Here the MEAN is: $\dfrac{\text{TOTAL number of organisms}}{\text{NUMBER of quadrats}} = \dfrac{154}{7} = 22$ daisies per quadrat

5) <u>Repeat</u> steps 1 to 4 in the <u>second</u> sample area.

6) Finally, <u>compare</u> the two means. E.g. you might find a mean of 2 daisies per m² in one area, and 22 daisies per m² (lots more) in another area.

## You Can Also Estimate the **Population Size** of an Organism **in an Area**

1) To work out the <u>population size</u> of an organism in a sample area, first you need to use a quadrat to find the <u>mean number of organisms per m²</u>. (If you use a quadrat with an area of 1 m², this is the same as the mean number of organisms per quadrat, as shown above.)

2) Then just <u>multiply the mean</u> by the <u>total area</u> of your sample area:

**Students used 0.5 m² quadrats to randomly sample daisies in a field. They found a mean of 10 daisies per quadrat. The area of the field was 800 m². Estimate the population of daisies in the field.**

1) Work out the <u>mean number of organisms per m²</u>.

$1 \div 0.5 = 2$
$2 \times 10 = 20$ daisies per m²

Because the quadrat is only 0.5 m², first you need to work out how many quadrats make up 1 m².

2) Then multiply the <u>mean</u> by the <u>total area</u> (in m²) of the habitat.

$20 \times 800$
$= 16\,000$ daisies on the field

 **Investigating Ecosystems**

So, now you think you've learnt <u>all about</u> quadrats. Well <u>hold on</u> — there's more <u>fun</u> to be had.

## Use **Belt Transects** to Study **Distribution Along** a **Gradient**

Sometimes <u>abiotic factors</u> will <u>change across a habitat</u>. The change is known as a <u>gradient</u>. You can use quadrats to help find out how organisms (like plants) are <u>distributed along</u> a gradient. For example, how a species becomes <u>more or less common</u> as you move from an area of <u>shade</u> (near a hedge at the edge of a field) to an area of full sun (the middle of the field). The quadrats are laid out along a <u>line</u>, forming a <u>belt transect</u>. Here's what you do:

1) <u>Mark out a line</u> in the area you want to study, e.g. from the hedge to the middle of the field.

2) Then <u>collect data</u> along the line using <u>quadrats</u> placed <u>next to</u> each other. If your transect is <u>long</u>, you could place the quadrats at <u>regular intervals</u> (e.g. every 2 metres) instead. Collect data by <u>counting</u> all the organisms of the species you're interested in, or by <u>estimating percentage cover</u>. This means estimating the <u>percentage area</u> of a quadrat covered by a particular type of organism.

Make sure you can correctly identify the organisms you're investigating. If necessary, use books or information from the internet to help you.

tape measure

quadrat 1

3) You could also <u>record</u> other data, such as the <u>mean height</u> of the plants you're counting or the <u>abiotic factors</u> in each quadrat (e.g. you could use a <u>light meter</u> to measure the light intensity).

4) <u>Repeat</u> steps 1 and 2 several times, then find the <u>mean</u> number of organisms or mean percentage cover for <u>each quadrat</u>.

5) Plot graphs to see if the <u>changing abiotic factor</u> is <u>correlated</u> with a change in the <u>distribution</u> of the species you're studying.

## Organisms have a relationship with their environment

**WORKING SCIENTIFICALLY** You could be asked to interpret some data showing the <u>relationship</u> between the distribution of a species and an abiotic factor. But remember, just because two things are <u>correlated</u>, it doesn't <u>always</u> mean a change in one is <u>causing</u> the change in the other. There might be <u>other factors</u> involved.

# Warm-Up and Exam Questions

This Ecosystems and Material Cycles topic's a long one — so make sure you've got these first few pages stuck in your head before moving on and learning the rest. These questions should help you.

## Warm-Up Questions

1) What is the correct scientific term for all the organisms of different species living in a habitat?
2) What is an ecosystem?
3) Give four examples of abiotic factors that could affect communities.

## Exam Questions

**PRACTICAL**

1 Some students investigated the distribution of poppies across a field next to a wood. A sketch of the area is shown in **Figure 1**.

Fence at edge of wood →

| Wood |
| --- |
| Field |

**Figure 1**

The students' results are shown in **Figure 2**.

| Number of poppies per m² | 5 | 9 | 14 | 19 | 26 |
| --- | --- | --- | --- | --- | --- |
| Distance from wood (m) | 2 | 4 | 6 | 8 | 10 |

**Figure 2**

(a) Describe how the students could have used quadrats to obtain the results in **Figure 2**.

*[3 marks]*

(b) Describe the trend in the results in **Figure 2**.

*[1 mark]*

2 Cutthroat trout are present in lakes in Yellowstone National Park. In the last few decades, lake trout have been introduced to the lakes. However, lake trout have emerged as predators and have been eating the cutthroat trout.

(a) Suggest and explain how the introduction of the lake trout might cause the population sizes of both species of fish to fluctuate over time.

*[4 marks]*

(b) Give **one** other biotic factor that could affect the size of the cutthroat trout population.

*[1 mark]*

# Human Impacts on Biodiversity

However you look at it, <u>humans</u> have a <u>big impact</u> on the environment, including on <u>biodiversity</u>.

## Human Activities Affect **Biodiversity**

1)  <u>Biodiversity</u> is the <u>variety of living organisms</u> in an <u>ecosystem</u>.

2)  Human <u>interactions</u> within ecosystems often affect biodiversity.

3)  Sometimes we have a <u>positive</u> impact on biodiversity (e.g. by carrying out <u>conservation schemes</u> or <u>reforestation</u>, see page 134), but we often have a <u>negative</u> effect.  Here are some examples:

## **Fertilisers** can Leach into **Water** and Cause **Eutrophication**

<u>Nitrates</u> are put onto fields as <u>fertilisers</u> (see p.141).  If <u>too much fertiliser</u> is applied and it <u>rains</u> afterwards, nitrates easily find their way into rivers and lakes.  The result is <u>eutrophication</u> — an <u>excess of nutrients</u> in water — which can lead to the <u>death</u> of many of the species present in the water, <u>reducing</u> the <u>biodiversity</u> of the habitat.  Here's how it happens:

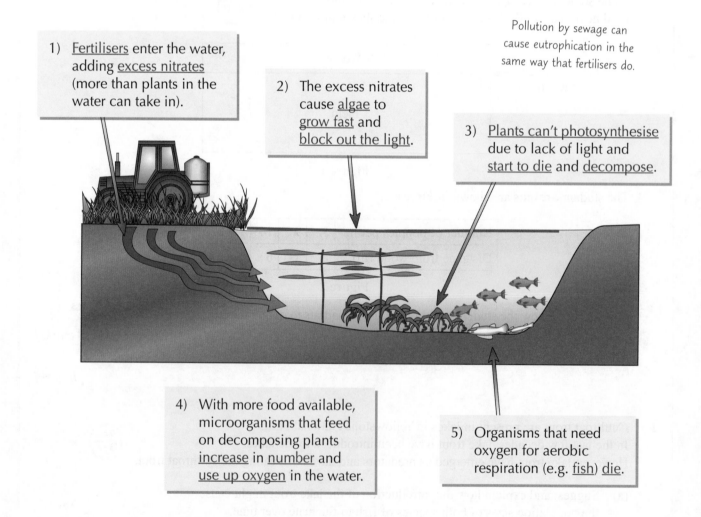

Pollution by sewage can cause eutrophication in the same way that fertilisers do.

1)  <u>Fertilisers</u> enter the water, adding <u>excess nitrates</u> (more than plants in the water can take in).

2)  The excess nitrates cause <u>algae</u> to <u>grow fast</u> and <u>block out the light</u>.

3)  <u>Plants can't photosynthesise</u> due to lack of light and <u>start to die</u> and <u>decompose</u>.

4)  With more food available, microorganisms that feed on decomposing plants <u>increase</u> in <u>number</u> and <u>use up oxygen</u> in the water.

5)  Organisms that need oxygen for aerobic respiration (e.g. <u>fish</u>) <u>die</u>.

## Fertilisers need to be used responsibly

Unfortunately, it's difficult to <u>stop using fertilisers</u> altogether because farmers worldwide are under pressure to <u>produce enough food</u> — and using fertilisers helps them <u>improve</u> their <u>crop yields</u>.
As you'll see on the next page our <u>demand</u> for <u>fish</u> is also <u>affecting</u> the <u>biodiversity</u> of our lakes and seas.

# Human Impacts on Biodiversity

## Fish can be Farmed in Holding Nets in Open Water

Fish farms in areas of open water (e.g. lakes or the sea) can reduce biodiversity in the surrounding area. It can happen like this:

1) Food is added to the nets to feed the fish, which produce huge amounts of waste. Both the food and the waste can leak into the open water, causing eutrophication and the death of wild species.

2) Fish farms in open water often act as a breeding ground for large numbers of parasites. These parasites can get out of the farm and infect wild animals, sometimes killing them.

3) Predators (e.g. sea lions) are attracted to the nets and can become trapped in them and die.

4) Sometimes farmed fish can escape into the wild, which can cause problems for wild populations of indigenous species (see below).

Sometimes fish are farmed in large tanks rather than in open water nets. These farms are low in biodiversity because often only one species is farmed, the tanks are often kept free of plants and predators, and any parasites and microorganisms are usually killed.

## The Introduction of Non-Indigenous Species Can Reduce Biodiversity

1) A non-indigenous species is one that doesn't naturally occur in an area. They can be introduced intentionally (e.g. for food or hunting) or unintentionally (e.g. as a stowaway in international cargo). The introduction of a non-indigenous species may cause problems for indigenous (native) species.

2) Non-indigenous species compete with indigenous species for resources like food and shelter. Sometimes, they are better at getting these resources and out-compete the indigenous species, which decrease in number and eventually die out. For example, signal crayfish were introduced to the UK for food, but they prey on and out-compete many indigenous river species, reducing biodiversity.

3) Non-indigenous species sometimes also bring new diseases to a habitat. These often infect and kill lots of indigenous species, reducing the habitat's biodiversity.

## Adding a new species to a habitat can reduce biodiversity

You'd think that introducing a new species into an ecosystem would increase biodiversity. But when they out-compete the indigenous species, the numbers of their competitors decline. And since many organisms in an ecosystem are interdependent (see p.127), this can have big knock-on effects in the community.

# Conservation and Biodiversity

Trying to conserve biodiversity can be tricky, given all the challenges that face different ecosystems (many of which are a result of human activities). There are benefits of doing this though, so it's pretty worthwhile...

## There Are **Lots** of Ways to **Conserve** and **Maintain** Biodiversity

Lots of human activities can reduce biodiversity (see the previous two pages). However, there are plenty of things that we can do to increase biodiversity. Here are a couple of examples...

### Reforestation Can Increase Biodiversity in **Deforested Areas**

1) Reforestation is when land where a forest previously stood is replanted to form a new forest.

2) Forests generally have a high biodiversity because they contain a wide variety of trees and other plants, and these provide food and shelter for lots of different animal species.

3) Deforestation reduces this biodiversity by removing the trees (either by chopping them down or burning them). Reforestation helps to restore it.

4) Reforestation programmes need to be carefully planned to maximise positive effects and minimise negative ones. For example, replanting a forest with a variety of tree species will result in a higher biodiversity than replanting using only a single type of tree.

### Conservation Schemes Protect At-Risk Species

1) Conservation schemes can help to protect biodiversity by preventing species from dying out.
2) Conservation methods include:

   1) Protecting a species' natural habitat (so that individuals have a place to live).
   2) Protecting species in safe areas outside of their natural habitat (e.g. animals can be protected in zoos) and introducing captive breeding programmes to increase numbers.
   3) The use of seed banks to store and distribute the seeds of rare and endangered plants.

## It's not all lost — biodiversity can be increased

There are ways in which we can improve the biodiversity of an area — but the scale of efforts to maintain or increase biodiversity often isn't large enough to combat the huge negative impact of other human activities.

# Conservation and Biodiversity

The last few pages have been all about what biodiversity is, how humans affect biodiversity and how we might go about maintaining it. But why is it important for us to maintain biodiversity? Read on...

## Maintaining Biodiversity Has Many Benefits

There are lots of benefits to both wildlife and humans of maintaining biodiversity on a local and global scale.

1) Protecting the human food supply — over-fishing has greatly reduced fish stocks in the world's oceans. Conservation programmes can ensure that future generations will have fish to eat.

2) Ensuring minimal damage to food chains — if one species becomes extinct it will affect all the organisms that feed on and are eaten by that species, so the whole food chain is affected. This means conserving one species may help others to survive.

3) Providing future medicines — many of the medicines we use today come from plants. Undiscovered plant species may contain new medicinal chemicals. If these plants are allowed to become extinct, e.g. through rainforest destruction, we could miss out on valuable medicines.

4) Cultural aspects — individual species may be important in a nation's or an area's cultural heritage, e.g. the bald eagle is being conserved in the USA as it is regarded as a national symbol.

5) Ecotourism — people are drawn to visit beautiful, unspoilt landscapes with a variety of animal and plant species. Ecotourism (environmentally-friendly tourism) helps bring money into biodiverse areas where conservation work is taking place.

6) Providing new jobs — things such as ecotourism, conservation schemes and reforestation schemes provide employment opportunities for local people.

## Biodiversity is important for us all

In some way or another the loss of biodiversity affects everyone — after all we are part of the biodiversity on earth. Make sure you know and can explain the benefits of maintaining biodiversity.

# Warm-Up and Exam Questions

You can't just stare at these pages and expect all of the information to go in. Do these questions to see how well you really know the stuff. If you get stuck you can always go back to the page for a quick recap.

## Warm-Up Questions

1) What is biodiversity?
2) Explain how excess nitrates in water systems can lead to the death of fish living in the water.
3) How do conservation schemes affect biodiversity? Explain your answer.
4) Describe two ways that an open water fish farm can reduce the biodiversity of an area.

## Exam Questions

1    Black rats were accidentally introduced into an island habitat by a tourist boat which visited the island. Local biologists are worried that the introduction of the non-indigenous rat species will have a negative impact on biodiversity.

Suggest and explain **two** ways that the introduction of black rats to the island could reduce biodiversity.

*[4 marks]*

2    A group of conservationists are working to replant the trees in an area of forest which has been badly damaged by a forest fire.

(a)   There is a suggestion that the whole area should be replanted with white spruce, a tree species which will be cheap to plant.
      Explain why only planting white spruce will result in low biodiversity.

*[2 marks]*

(b)   Several years after the area was successfully reforested, the conservationists found a few individuals of an endangered small mammal species living in the forest. The conservationists want to protect the species. Suggest **one** way they could do this.

*[1 mark]*

3*   Human activity has reduced the rainforest cover in Ecuador significantly. Deforestation has reduced biodiversity and endangered certain animal and plant species that are only found in Ecuador.

Some conservation schemes have been set up which employ local people to protect at-risk species found in the rainforest.

Discuss why conservation schemes like this may be beneficial.
In your answer you should include ideas about the potential benefits to plants and animals in the ecosystem, the people of Ecuador and people from other countries.

*[6 marks]*

# The Carbon Cycle

Recycling may be a buzz word for us but it's old school for nature. All the nutrients in our environment are constantly being recycled — there's a nice balance between what goes in and what goes out again.

## Materials are Constantly Recycled in an Ecosystem

1) An ecosystem is all the organisms living in an area, as well as all the non-living conditions, e.g. soil quality, availability of water, temperature.

*There's more on ecosystems on page 127.*

2) Materials are recycled through both the living (biotic) and non-living (abiotic) components of ecosystems:

> 1) Living things are made of elements they take from the environment, e.g. plants take in carbon and oxygen from the air and nitrogen from the soil.
>
> 2) They turn these elements into the complex compounds (carbohydrates, proteins and fats) that make up living organisms. Elements are passed along food chains when animals eat the plants and each other.
>
> 3) The elements are recycled — waste products and dead organisms are broken down by decomposers (usually microorganisms) and the elements in them are returned to the soil or air, ready to be taken in by new plants and put back into the food chain.

## The Carbon Cycle Shows How Carbon is Recycled

Carbon is an important element in the materials that living things are made from. But there's only a fixed amount of carbon in the world. This means it's constantly recycled:

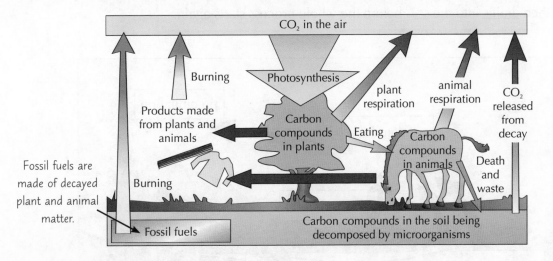

This diagram isn't half as bad as it looks. Learn these important points:

> 1) There's only one arrow going down from $CO_2$ in the air. The whole thing is 'powered' by photosynthesis. Green plants use the carbon from $CO_2$ to make carbohydrates, fats and proteins.
>
> 2) Eating passes the carbon compounds in the plants along to animals in a food chain.
>
> 3) Both plant and animal respiration while the organisms are alive releases $CO_2$ back into the air.
>
> 4) Plants and animals eventually die and decompose, or are killed and turned into useful products.
>
> 5) When plants and animals decompose they're broken down by microorganisms, like bacteria and fungi. These decomposers release $CO_2$ into the air by respiration, as they break down the material.
>
> 6) Some useful plant and animal products, e.g. wood and fossil fuels, are burned (combustion). This process also releases $CO_2$ back into the air.
>
> 7) Decomposition of materials means that habitats can be maintained for the organisms that live there, e.g. nutrients are returned to the soil, and waste material, such as dead leaves, doesn't just pile up.

# The Water Cycle

The <u>amount</u> of water on Earth is pretty much <u>constant</u> — but <u>where</u> it is changes.
Water moves between <u>rivers</u>, <u>lakes</u>, <u>oceans</u> and the <u>atmosphere</u> in what's known as the <u>water cycle</u>.

## The **Water Cycle** Means Water is **Endlessly Recycled**

The water here on planet Earth is constantly <u>recycled</u>.
There are four key steps you should understand:

As warm water vapour rises it
cools down and forms clouds.

1) <u>Energy</u> from the <u>Sun</u> makes water <u>evaporate</u> from the land and sea, turning it into <u>water vapour</u>. Water also evaporates from plants — this is known as <u>transpiration</u> (see p.95).

2) The warm water vapour is <u>carried upwards</u> (as warm air rises). When it gets higher up it <u>cools</u> and <u>condenses</u> to form <u>clouds</u>.

3) Water falls from the clouds as <u>precipitation</u> (usually rain, but sometimes snow or hail) onto <u>land</u>, where it provides <u>fresh water</u> for <u>plants</u> and <u>animals</u>.

4) It then <u>drains</u> into the <u>sea</u>, before the whole process starts again.

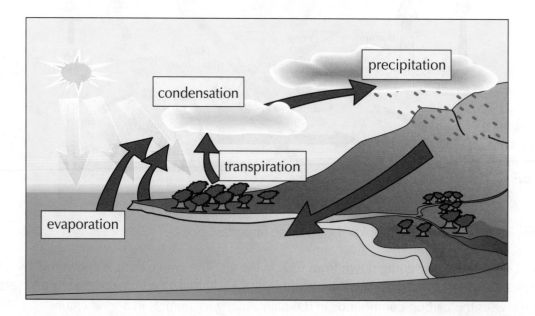

If it wasn't for the water cycle constantly recycling water, we'd quickly <u>run out</u> of the stuff.
That would be <u>really bad</u> news because all living things on our planet <u>need</u> water to <u>survive</u>.

## Evaporation, transpiration, condensation, precipitation

The water cycle is pretty straightforward, so there's absolutely no excuse not to learn it inside out.
The most important thing to remember is that it's a <u>cycle</u> — a <u>continuous</u> process with no beginning or end.
Water that falls to the ground as rain (or snow, hail etc.) will eventually end up back in the clouds again.

# The Water Cycle

## A **Drought** Occurs When There **Isn't Enough Precipitation**

Droughts can cause <u>big problems</u>, partly because we rely on <u>precipitation</u> to get <u>fresh water</u> for <u>drinking</u> (sea water is too salty). Luckily, in times of drought, there are methods we can use to produce <u>potable water</u> (water that's suitable for drinking). One of these methods is called <u>desalination</u>.

## **Desalination** Can Be Used to Produce **Potable Water** From **Salt Water**

Desalination removes <u>salts</u> (<u>mineral ions</u>) from salt water (e.g. sea water). There are a few <u>different methods</u> of desalination. One really <u>simple</u> method is <u>thermal desalination</u>:

1) Salt water is <u>boiled</u> in a large enclosed vessel, so that the water <u>evaporates</u>.
2) The steam <u>rises</u> to the top of the vessel, but the salts stay at the <u>bottom</u>.
3) The steam then travels down a pipe from the top of the vessel and cools and <u>condenses</u> back into <u>pure water</u>.

## **Reverse Osmosis** is a Widely Used Modern Method of **Desalination**

1) <u>Osmosis</u> is the net movement of <u>water</u> across a <u>partially permeable membrane</u>, from an area of <u>HIGHER water concentration</u> to an area of <u>LOWER water concentration</u> (see page 33).

2) The <u>higher</u> the <u>salt concentration</u> in a solution, the <u>lower</u> the <u>water concentration</u>, so you could also say that osmosis is the net movement of water from an area of <u>LOWER salt concentration</u> to an area of <u>HIGHER salt concentration</u>.

3) <u>Reverse osmosis</u> reverses this process to <u>get rid of impurities</u> in water. Here's how:

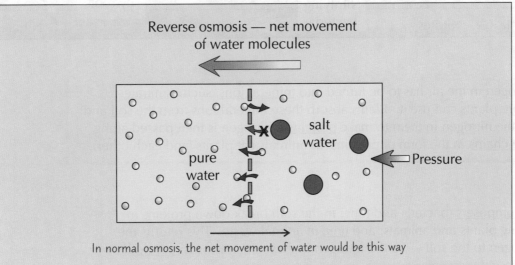

Reverse osmosis — net movement of water molecules

pure water

salt water

Pressure

In normal osmosis, the net movement of water would be this way

1) Salt water is first <u>treated</u> to remove solids, before being fed at a very <u>high pressure</u> into a vessel containing a <u>partially permeable membrane</u>.

2) The pressure causes the water molecules to move in the <u>opposite direction</u> to <u>osmosis</u> — from a <u>higher salt concentration</u> to a <u>lower salt concentration</u>.

3) As the water is forced through the membrane, the <u>salts</u> are <u>left behind</u>, <u>removing</u> them from the water.

# The Nitrogen Cycle

Just like carbon and water, nitrogen is constantly being <u>recycled</u>.

## Nitrogen is Recycled in the Nitrogen Cycle

1) The <u>atmosphere</u> contains <u>78% nitrogen gas</u>, $N_2$. This is <u>very unreactive</u> and so it can't be used <u>directly</u> by plants or animals. <u>Nitrogen</u> is <u>needed</u> for making <u>proteins</u> for growth, so living organisms have to get it somehow.

2) <u>Nitrogen</u> is passed back and forth between the air, living organisms and the soil in the <u>nitrogen cycle</u>. Here's a diagram showing how it works. (Don't worry, it's all explained in more detail below.)

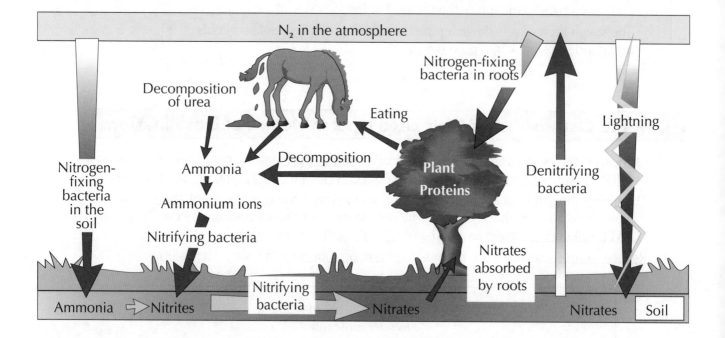

3) Nitrogen in the air has to be turned into <u>mineral ions</u>, such as <u>nitrates</u>, before plants can use it. Plants absorb these mineral ions from the <u>soil</u> and use the nitrogen in them to make <u>proteins</u>. Nitrogen is then passed along <u>food chains</u> in the form of proteins, as animals eat plants (and each other).

4) <u>Decomposers</u> (bacteria and fungi in the soil) break down <u>proteins</u> in rotting plants and animals, and <u>urea</u> in animal waste. This returns the nitrogen to the soil — so the nitrogen in these organisms is <u>recycled</u>.

5) <u>Nitrogen fixation</u> is the process of turning <u>$N_2$ from the air</u> into <u>nitrogen-containing ions</u> in the soil which <u>plants can use</u>. There are <u>two main ways</u> that this happens:

   a) <u>Lightning</u> — there's so much <u>energy</u> in a bolt of lightning that it's enough to make nitrogen <u>react with oxygen</u> in the air to give nitrates.

   b) <u>Nitrogen-fixing bacteria</u> in roots and soil (see next page).

# The Nitrogen Cycle

6) There are <u>four</u> different types of <u>bacteria</u> involved in the nitrogen cycle:

1) <u>DECOMPOSERS</u> — decompose <u>proteins</u> and <u>urea</u> and turn them into <u>ammonia</u>. Ammonia forms <u>ammonium ions</u> in solution that plants can use.

2) <u>NITRIFYING BACTERIA</u> — turn <u>ammonia</u> in decaying matter into <u>nitrites</u> and then into <u>nitrates</u>. Different species of nitrifying bacteria are responsible for producing nitrites and nitrates.

3) <u>NITROGEN-FIXING BACTERIA</u> — turn <u>atmospheric $N_2$</u> into <u>ammonia</u>, which forms <u>ammonium ions</u>.

4) <u>DENITRIFYING BACTERIA</u> — turn <u>nitrates</u> back into $N_2$ gas. This is of no benefit to living organisms. Denitrifying bacteria are often found in <u>waterlogged soils</u>.

7) Some <u>nitrogen-fixing bacteria</u> live in the <u>soil</u>. Others live in <u>nodules</u> on the roots of <u>legume plants</u> (e.g. peas and beans). When these plants <u>decompose</u>, the nitrogen <u>stored</u> in them and in their <u>nodules</u> is returned to the soil. Nitrogen-containing ions can also <u>leak out</u> of the nodules <u>during plant growth</u>. The plants have a <u>mutualistic relationship</u> (see page 127) with the bacteria — the bacteria get <u>food</u> (sugars) from the plant, and the plant gets <u>nitrogen-containing ions</u> from the bacteria to make into <u>proteins</u>.

## Farmers Can Increase the Amount of Nitrates in the Soil

1) Like all plants, crops take up <u>nitrates</u> from the soil as they grow.

2) But crops are <u>harvested</u>, rather than being left to <u>die</u> and <u>decompose</u>, so the nitrogen they contain <u>isn't returned</u> to the soil.

3) Over time, the nitrogen content of the soil <u>decreases</u>, leading to <u>poor crop growth</u> and <u>deficiency diseases</u>.

4) So farmers have ways of increasing the amount of nitrates in the soil to help their crops <u>grow better</u>:

### Crop Rotation

This is where, instead of growing the same crop in a field year after year, <u>different crops</u> are grown each year in a <u>cycle</u>. The cycle usually includes a <u>nitrogen-fixing</u> crop (e.g. peas or beans), which helps to put nitrates back into the soil for another crop to use the following year.

### Fertilisers

Spreading <u>animal manure</u> or <u>compost</u> on fields <u>recycles</u> the nutrients left in plant and animal waste and returns them to the soil through <u>decomposition</u>. <u>Artificial fertilisers</u> containing <u>nitrates</u> (and other mineral ions needed by plants) can also be used, but these can be <u>expensive</u> and can cause <u>environmental problems</u> (see page 132).

## Bacteria do a lot of the hard work in the nitrogen cycle

Different types of <u>bacteria</u> play <u>different roles</u> at <u>different points</u> in the <u>nitrogen cycle</u>. You definitely need to get your head around which type of bacteria does what. Make sure that you know before moving on.

# Warm-Up and Exam Questions

You know the drill, first some warm-up questions to ease you in, then the slightly trickier exam questions.

## Warm-Up Questions

1) How is the carbon that is stored in fossil fuels returned to the atmosphere?
2) Describe how thermal desalination can be used to produce potable water.
3) Describe the role of nitrifying bacteria in the nitrogen cycle.
4) Explain why using nitrogen-containing fertilisers can be beneficial to farmers.

## Exam Questions

1 **Figure 1** shows a simplified version of part of the nitrogen cycle.

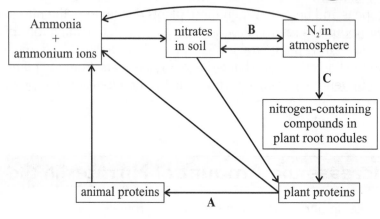

**Figure 1**

(a) Describe what is happening at stage **A**.

*[1 mark]*

(b) Name the type of bacteria responsible for stage **B**.

*[1 mark]*

(c) Name the type of bacteria responsible for stage **C**.

*[1 mark]*

2 The water cycle describes the constant movement of water molecules on the Earth.

(a) In the water cycle, name the process by which water moves from plants into the air.

*[1 mark]*

(b) Describe the shortest route a water molecule could take
through the water cycle to get from an ocean to a garden pond.

*[4 marks]*

3* An area of woodland is cleared to build a house. The tree trunks are taken away to be
dried and used in furniture making. The smaller tree branches are used for firewood.
The green plants are piled up at the edge of the building site and left there.

Describe how carbon stored in the vegetation that has been cleared could be returned to the atmosphere.

*[6 marks]*

# Revision Summary for Topic 9

Congratulations, you've made it to the end of <u>Topic 9</u> — now it's time to test how much you've taken in...
* Try these questions and <u>tick off each one</u> when you <u>get it right</u>.
* When you've done <u>all the questions</u> under a heading and are <u>completely happy</u> with it, tick it off.

## Ecosystems (p.127-130) ☑

1) Define the following terms:   a) population,   b) community. ☑
2) What does it mean if two species are interdependent? ☑
3) Give an example of a mutualistic relationship. ☑
4) Give two biotic factors and explain how each one could affect a community. ☑
5) Briefly describe how you could use quadrats to investigate the population size of a species. ☑
6) What is a belt transect? ☑

## Biodiversity (p.132-135) ☑

7) a)  What is meant by the term 'eutrophication'? ☑
   b)  Explain how having an open water fish farm in a water system can cause eutrophication. ☑
8) What is a non-indigenous species? ☑
9) Give three examples of types of conservation schemes. ☑
10) Give three benefits of maintaining biodiversity. ☑

## The Carbon, Water and Nitrogen Cycles (p.137-141) ☑

11) Name the only process that removes carbon dioxide from the air in the carbon cycle. ☑
12) Name two processes that put carbon dioxide back into the air in the carbon cycle. ☑
13) Produce a labelled diagram of the water cycle. ☑
14) Why is the ability to produce potable water important in times of drought? ☑
15) What does desalination mean? ☑
16) Name a common method of desalination. ☑
17) Describe the role of nitrogen-fixing bacteria in the nitrogen cycle. ☑
18) What is crop rotation?  Why is it beneficial to farmers? ☑

# Safety and Ethics

Science can be quite dangerous at times, so it's important that you keep yourself (and others) <u>safe</u> in the lab. Some experiments can also involve <u>ethical issues</u> that you must deal with respectfully and responsibly.

## Make Sure You're **Working Safely** in the **Lab**

1) <u>Before</u> you start any experiment, make sure you know about any <u>safety precautions</u> to do with your <u>method</u> or the <u>chemicals</u> you're using. You need to <u>follow</u> any instructions that your teacher gives you <u>carefully</u>. The chemicals you're using may be <u>hazardous</u> — for example, they might be <u>flammable</u> (<u>catch fire easily</u>), or they might <u>irritate</u> or <u>burn</u> your <u>skin</u> if it comes into contact with them.

2) Make sure that you're wearing <u>sensible clothing</u> when you're in the lab (e.g. open shoes won't protect your feet from spillages). When you're doing an experiment, you should wear a <u>lab coat</u> to protect your skin and clothing. Depending on the experiment, you may need to also wear <u>safety goggles</u> and <u>gloves</u>.

3) You also need to be aware of <u>general safety</u> in the lab, e.g. keep anything <u>flammable</u> away from lit Bunsen burners, don't directly touch any <u>hot equipment</u>, handle <u>glassware</u> (including microscope slides) carefully to <u>avoid breakages</u>, etc.

## You Need to Think About **Ethical Issues** In Your Experiments

1) Any <u>organisms</u> involved in your investigations need to be treated <u>safely</u> and <u>ethically</u>.

2) <u>Animals</u> need to be treated <u>humanely</u> — they should be <u>handled carefully</u> and any wild animals captured for studying should be <u>returned to their original habitat</u>. Any animals kept in the lab should also be <u>cared for</u> in a humane way, e.g. they should not be kept in conditions that are <u>too hot</u>.

3) If you are carrying out an experiment involving other <u>students</u>, they should not be forced to participate <u>against their will</u> or feel <u>pressured</u> to take part.

## BEWARE — hazardous biology experiments about...

<u>Before</u> you carry out an experiment, you must <u>consider all of the hazards</u>. They can be anything from <u>chemicals</u> to <u>sharp objects</u>, <u>pathogens</u> to <u>heating equipment</u>. Whatever the hazard, make sure you know all the <u>safety precautions</u> you should follow to keep yourself, and others, safe.

# Heating Substances

Some more useful lab stuff for you now — a bit about <u>heating things up</u>.

## Bunsen Burners Have a **Naked Flame**

Bunsen burners are good for <u>heating things quickly</u>. But you need to make sure you're using them <u>safely</u>:

- You should always use a Bunsen burner on a <u>heat-proof mat</u>.
- If your Bunsen burner is alight but not heating anything, make sure you <u>close</u> the hole so that the flame becomes <u>yellow</u> and <u>clearly visible</u>.
- Use the <u>blue</u> flame to heat things. If you're heating a vessel <u>in</u> the flame, hold it at the <u>top</u> (e.g. with <u>tongs</u>) and point the opening <u>away from</u> yourself (and others).
- If you're heating something <u>over</u> the flame (e.g. a beaker of water), you should put a <u>tripod and gauze</u> over the Bunsen burner before you light it, and place the vessel on this.
- Whenever you use a Bunsen burner, you should wear <u>safety goggles</u> to protect your eyes.

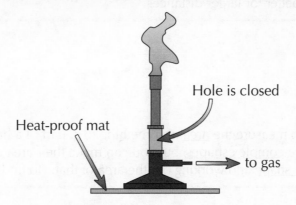

Hole is closed

Heat-proof mat

to gas

## The Temperature of **Electric Water Baths** Can Be **Set**

1) A <u>water bath</u> is a container filled with water that can be heated to a <u>specific temperature</u>. A <u>simple</u> water bath can be made by heating a <u>beaker of water</u> over a <u>Bunsen burner</u> and monitoring the temperature with a <u>thermometer</u> (see p.28). However, it is difficult to keep the temperature of the water <u>constant</u>.

2) An <u>electric water bath</u> will monitor and adjust the temperature for you. It's a much easier way of keeping the temperature of a reaction mixture constant. Here's how you use one:

- <u>Set</u> the temperature on the water bath, and allow the water to <u>heat up</u>.
- To make sure it's reached the right temperature, use a <u>thermometer</u>.
- Place the vessel containing your substance in the water bath using <u>test tube holders</u> or <u>tongs</u>. The level of water outside the vessel should be <u>just above</u> the level of the substance in the vessel.
- The substance will then be warmed to the <u>same temperature</u> as the water. As the substance in the vessel is surrounded by water, the heating is very <u>even</u>.

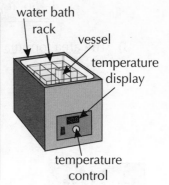

water bath rack

vessel

temperature display

temperature control

## Electric water baths are great for keeping the temperature constant

Make sure you're clear on how to use <u>Bunsen burners</u> and <u>electric water baths</u>, and more importantly, on how to use them <u>safely</u>. Obviously flames and hot things are <u>very dangerous</u>, so <u>take care</u>.

# Measuring Substances

Get your lab coats on, it's time to find out about some of the skills you'll need in experiments...

## Use the **Right Apparatus** to Take **Accurate Readings**

### 1. Length

1) Length can be measured in different units (e.g. mm, cm, m). Smaller units have a higher degree of accuracy. For example, it's more accurate to measure the length of a potato cylinder to the nearest mm than the nearest cm.

2) You'll need to decide on the appropriate level of accuracy for your experiment. For example, the length of a leaf would be better measured in millimetres, but the length of a transect line would be better measured in metres.

3) It is also important to choose the right equipment when measuring length — a ruler would probably be best for small things, but a metre rule or tape measure would be better for larger distances.

### 2. Area

In biology, you might need to measure the area of something (e.g. part of a habitat, a living thing). Living things are usually quite complex shapes, but you can make their area easier to work out by comparing them to a simpler shape and working out the area of that. To find the area of something:

1) First, you'll need to take accurate measurements of its dimensions.

> If you want to measure the area of a field (see page 129) that is rectangular, you'll need to use a tape measure or a trundle wheel to measure the length and width of the field. Record your readings in metres.

2) Then you can calculate its area.

> Area of a rectangle = length × width.
> So, if your field is 30 m by 55 m, the area would be $30 \times 55 = \underline{1650 \ m^2}$.

*Don't forget the units of area are always something squared, e.g. mm².*

3) The area formula for a triangle may also come in useful:

### Area of a triangle = ½ × base × height

### 3. Mass

To weigh a substance, start by putting the container you are weighing your substance into on a balance. Set the balance to exactly zero and then weigh out the correct amount of your substance.

# Measuring Substances

## 4. Time

1) If your experiment involves <u>timing</u> something (e.g. how long a reaction takes to happen) or taking measurements at <u>regular intervals</u>, it's probably best to use a <u>stopwatch</u>.

2) Using a <u>stopwatch</u> that measures to the nearest <u>0.1 s</u> will make your results more <u>accurate</u>.

3) Always make sure you <u>start</u> and <u>stop</u> the stopwatch at exactly the right time. For example, if you're investigating the rate of a reaction, you should start timing at the <u>exact moment</u> you mix the reagents and start the reaction.

4) It's a good idea to get the <u>same person</u> to do the timing so the results are as <u>precise</u> as possible.

## 5. Temperature

1) You can use a <u>thermometer</u> to measure temperature.

2) Make sure that the <u>bulb</u> of the thermometer is <u>completely submerged</u> in the substance you're measuring and that you wait for the temperature to <u>stabilise</u> before you take your initial reading.

3) Read off the <u>scale</u> on the thermometer at <u>eye level</u> to make sure your reading is correct.

*When you're reading off a scale, write down the value of the graduation that the amount is closest to. If it's exactly halfway between two values, round up.*

## 6. Volume of a Liquid

There's more than one way to measure the volume of a <u>liquid</u>. Whichever method you use, always read the volume from the <u>bottom of the meniscus</u> (the curved upper surface of the liquid) when it's at <u>eye level</u>.

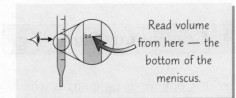

*Read volume from here — the bottom of the meniscus.*

### Using a pipette

1) <u>Pipettes</u> are used to suck up and <u>transfer</u> volumes of liquid between containers.

2) <u>Dropping pipettes</u> are used to transfer <u>drops</u> of liquid.

3) <u>Graduated pipettes</u> are used to transfer <u>accurate</u> volumes.

4) A <u>pipette filler</u> is attached to the end of a graduated pipette, to <u>control</u> the amount of liquid being drawn up.

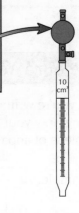

### Using a measuring cylinder

1) <u>Measuring cylinders</u> come in all different <u>sizes</u>.

2) Make sure you choose one that's the right size for the measurement you want to make. It's no good using a huge 1 dm³ cylinder to measure out 2 cm³ of a liquid — the graduations will be too big, and you'll end up with <u>massive errors</u>. It'd be much better to use one that measures up to 10 cm³.

# Measuring Substances

## 7. **Volume** of a **Gas**

1) To accurately measure the <u>volume</u> of gas, you should use a <u>gas syringe</u>.
2) Alternatively, you can use an <u>upturned measuring cylinder</u> filled with <u>water</u>. The gas will <u>displace</u> the water so you can <u>read the volume</u> off the <u>scale</u>.
3) You could also <u>count the bubbles</u> of gas released. But the bubbles could be <u>different sizes</u> and if they're produced quickly you might <u>miss some</u> — so this method is <u>less accurate</u>.
4) When you're measuring a gas, you need to make sure that the equipment is set up so that none of the gas can <u>escape</u>, otherwise your results won't be <u>accurate</u>.

## 8. **pH**

The method you should use to measure pH depends on what your experiment is.

1) <u>Indicators</u> are dyes that <u>change colour</u> depending on whether they're in an <u>acid</u> or an <u>alkali</u>. You use them by adding a couple of drops of the indicator to the solution you're interested in. <u>Universal indicator</u> is a <u>mixture</u> of indicators that changes colour <u>gradually</u> as pH changes. It's useful for <u>estimating</u> the pH of a solution based on its colour.
2) <u>Indicator paper</u> is useful if you don't want to colour the entire solution that you're testing. It <u>changes colour</u> depending on the pH of the solution it touches. You can also hold a piece of <u>damp indicator paper</u> in a <u>gas sample</u> to test its pH.
3) <u>pH meters</u> have a <u>digital display</u> that gives an <u>accurate value</u> for the pH of a solution.

*Blue litmus paper turns <u>red</u> in acidic conditions and red litmus paper turns <u>blue</u> in alkaline conditions.*

## 9. **Continuous Sampling**

1) <u>Continuous sampling</u> is when <u>lots of samples</u> are taken at <u>regular intervals</u> over a particular time period. This means you can see what is happening <u>during the experiment</u>, not just its outcome.
2) Using a <u>data logger</u> connected to a computer is an <u>example</u> of continuous sampling. Data loggers can be used to measure a range of variables, including <u>temperature</u>, <u>pH</u> and <u>O$_2$ concentration</u>.

## Make Sure You Can **Draw Diagrams** of Your Equipment

When you're writing out a <u>method</u> for your experiment, it's always a good idea to draw a <u>labelled diagram</u> showing how your apparatus will be <u>set up</u>. The easiest way to do this is to use a scientific drawing, where each piece of apparatus is drawn as if you're looking at its <u>cross-section</u> (with no shading or colouring).

For example:

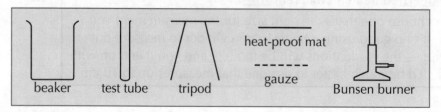

*The pieces of glassware are drawn without tops so they aren't sealed. If you want to draw a closed system, remember to draw a bung in the top.*

## Practice Exams

Once you've been through all the questions in this book, you should feel pretty confident about the exams.
As final preparation, here is a set of **practice exams** to really get you set for the real thing. The time allowed for
each paper is 1 hour 10 minutes. These papers are designed to give you the best possible preparation for your exams.

*CGP*    Practice Exam Paper
GCSE Combined Science

# GCSE Combined Science

## Biology Paper 1

## *Higher Tier*

In addition to this paper you should have:
- A ruler.
- A calculator.

| Centre name | | | | |
|---|---|---|---|---|
| Centre number | | | | |
| Candidate number | | | | |

**Time allowed:**
- 1 hour 10 minutes

| Surname |
|---|
| Other names |
| Candidate signature |

**Instructions to candidates**
- Write your name and other details in the spaces provided above.
- Answer **all** questions in the spaces provided.
- Do all rough work on the paper.
- Cross out any work you do not want to be marked.
- You are allowed to use a calculator.

**Information for candidates**
- The marks available are given in brackets at the end of each question.
- There are 60 marks available for this paper.
- You should use good English and present your answers in a
  clear and organised way.
- For questions marked with an asterisk (*) ensure that your answers
  have a logical structure, with points that link together clearly, and
  include detailed, relevant information.

**Advice to candidates**
- In calculations show clearly how you worked out your answers.
- Read each question carefully before answering it.
- Check your answers if you have time.

### For examiner's use

| Q | Attempt Nº | | | Q | Attempt Nº | | |
|---|---|---|---|---|---|---|---|
| | 1 | 2 | 3 | | 1 | 2 | 3 |
| 1 | | | | 4 | | | |
| 2 | | | | 5 | | | |
| 3 | | | | 6 | | | |
| | | | Total | | | | |

1   **Figure 1** shows an animal cell.

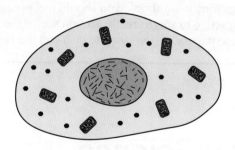

**Figure 1**

(a) Give **two** ways in which the cell in **Figure 1** is different from a bacterial cell.

.......................................................................................................................................................

.......................................................................................................................................................

.......................................................................................................................................................

*[2 marks]*

(b) Not all animal cells have the same structures as the cell in **Figure 1**.
Explain why.

.......................................................................................................................................................

.......................................................................................................................................................

*[1 mark]*

**Figure 2** shows a single-celled organism called *Euglena*, found in pond water.

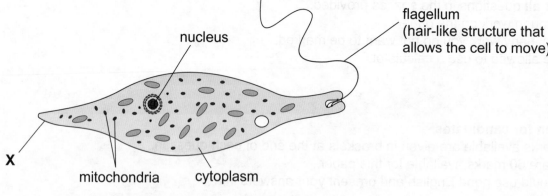

**Figure 2**

(c) What is the name of the subcellular structure labelled **X**?

☐ **A** ribosome

☐ **B** chloroplast

☐ **C** vacuole

☐ **D** cell membrane

*[1 mark]*

**(d)** A scientist viewed an individual *Euglena* under a microscope with × 150 magnification.
He calculated the real length of the *Euglena* to be 0.054 mm.
Calculate the length of the image of the *Euglena* in mm.  Use the formula:

$$\text{magnification} = \frac{\text{image size}}{\text{real size}}$$

............................ mm

*[2 marks]*

**(e)** When *Euglena* was first discovered, scientists disagreed over whether it was
a plant or an animal.
Give **two** similarities and **two** differences between plant and animal cells.

........................................................................................................................

........................................................................................................................

........................................................................................................................

........................................................................................................................

........................................................................................................................

........................................................................................................................

........................................................................................................................

*[4 marks]*

*[Total 10 marks]*

**Turn over for the next question**

**Turn over ▶**

2   Communicable diseases can be spread between individuals.

(a) Zika virus disease is an example of a communicable disease.
The virus that causes the disease is spread by a mosquito vector.
Suggest **two** ways that the spread of the Zika virus disease could be reduced.

.......................................................................................................................................................

.......................................................................................................................................................

.......................................................................................................................................................

*[2 marks]*

(b) Which of the following communicable diseases is also spread by a vector?

☐  **A**  influenza

☐  **B**  malaria

☐  **C**  HIV

☐  **D**  athlete's foot

*[1 mark]*

(c) Tuberculosis (TB) is a communicable disease caused by *Mycobacterium tuberculosis*
bacteria.  A strain of this bacteria was observed to have cells that divided every
18 hours on average.

Give the number of cells that would be produced from one bacterium of this strain
in 3 days.

.................................................... cells
*[2 marks]*

**(d)** The TB vaccine protects against tuberculosis.
Explain how immunisation helps to protect the body against a disease.

.................................................................................................................................

.................................................................................................................................

.................................................................................................................................

.................................................................................................................................

.................................................................................................................................

.................................................................................................................................

.................................................................................................................................

.................................................................................................................................

*[4 marks]*

*[Total 9 marks]*

**Turn over for the next question**

**Turn over ▶**

**3** Research from the Human Genome Project can be used to improve human health.

**(a)** What is meant by the term 'genome'?

☐ **A** A section of DNA that codes for a particular protein.

☐ **B** All of an organism's DNA.

☐ **C** A long coiled up molecule of DNA.

☐ **D** A unit containing a sugar molecule, a phosphate molecule and a base.

*[1 mark]*

Cystic fibrosis is an inherited disorder caused by a recessive allele.

**(b)** Suggest how the Human Genome Project could have the potential to help people with cystic fibrosis.

.................................................................................................................................................

.................................................................................................................................................

*[1 mark]*

A couple have a baby boy. The doctor tells them that the baby has inherited cystic fibrosis. Neither parent shows signs of the disorder.

**(c)** In the space below, construct a diagram to show how the baby inherited cystic fibrosis.

Your diagram should show the genotypes of both parents, the genotypes of their gametes, and all the possible genotypes of their offspring.

Use **F** to represent the dominant allele and **f** to represent the recessive allele.

*[3 marks]*

The family pedigree in **Figure 3** shows a family with a history of cystic fibrosis.

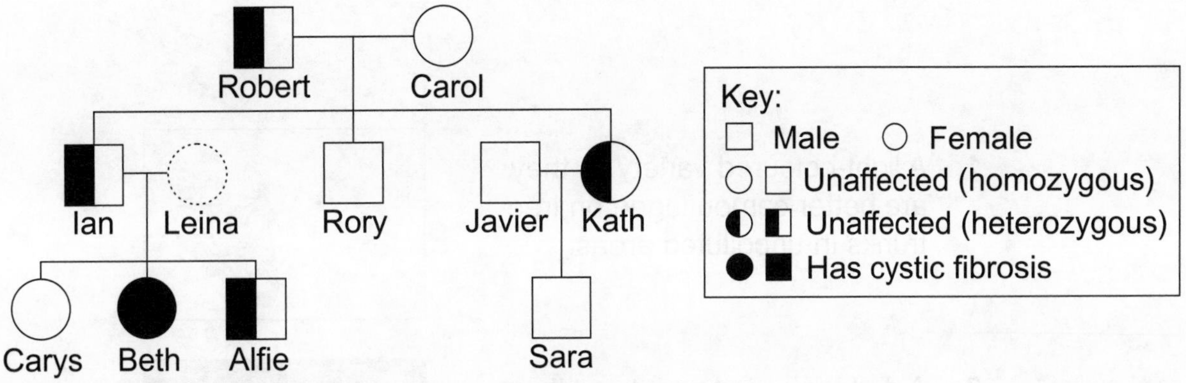

**Figure 3**

**(d)** Using the information in **Figure 3**, state what Leina's genotype must be.
Explain your answer.

..........................................................................................................................................

..........................................................................................................................................

..........................................................................................................................................

..........................................................................................................................................

*[2 marks]*

**(e)** Carys and Beth are sisters. Carys has a scar on her hand. Beth does not.

Explain whether this is an example of genetic variation, environmental variation, or a combination of both.

..........................................................................................................................................

..........................................................................................................................................

..........................................................................................................................................

*[2 marks]*

*[Total 9 marks]*

**Turn over for the next question**

**Turn over ▶**

**4** The peppered moth is an insect that lives on the trunks of trees in Britain.
The moths are prey for birds such as thrushes.
The peppered moth exists in two varieties, shown in **Figure 4**.

1. A light-coloured variety — they are better camouflaged on tree trunks in unpolluted areas.

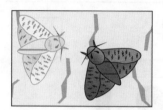

2. A dark-coloured variety — they are better camouflaged on sooty tree trunks in badly polluted areas.

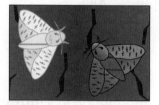

**Figure 4**

The bar charts in **Figure 5** show the percentages of dark- and light-coloured peppered moths in two different towns.

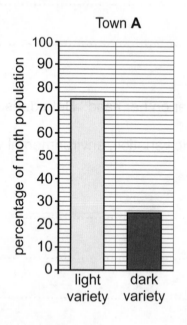
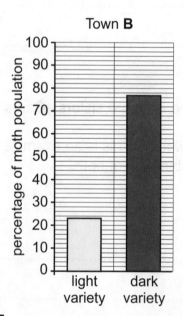

**Figure 5**

**(a)** State which town, **A** or **B**, is the most polluted. Give a reason for your answer.

..............................................................................................................................................

..............................................................................................................................................

*[1 mark]*

**(b)** Calculate the difference in percentage between the dark-coloured moth population in Town **A** and Town **B**. Show your working.

.............................%

*[2 marks]*

Collecting the data shown in **Figure 5** involved leaving traps overnight, with lights inside to attract moths. The scientists then counted the moths that had been captured, before releasing them.

**(c)** Suggest **one** way that the scientists carrying out this investigation could have helped to ensure the humane treatment of the moths.

..................................................................................................................................

..................................................................................................................................

*[1 mark]*

The dark variety of the moth was first recorded in the north of England in 1848. It became increasingly common in polluted areas until the 1960s, when the number of soot-covered trees declined because of the introduction of new laws.

**(d)** Using the idea of natural selection, explain why the dark variety of moth became more common in soot-polluted areas.

..................................................................................................................................

..................................................................................................................................

..................................................................................................................................

..................................................................................................................................

..................................................................................................................................

..................................................................................................................................

..................................................................................................................................

..................................................................................................................................

*[4 marks]*

*[Total 8 marks]*

**Turn over for the next question**

**Turn over ▶**

**5** A student did an experiment to investigate the effect of pH on the action of the enzyme amylase. The method used is shown in **Figure 6**.

> 1. Add a set quantity of starch solution to a test tube and the same quantity of amylase solution to another.
> 2. Add a set quantity of a buffer solution with a pH of 5 to the tube containing starch solution.
> 3. Place all of the test tubes in a water bath at 35 °C.
> 4. Allow the starch and amylase solutions to reach the temperature of the water bath, then mix them together and return the mixture to the water bath.
> 5. Take a small sample of the mixture every minute and test for starch.
> 6. Stop the experiment when starch is no longer present in the sample, or after 30 minutes (whichever is sooner).
> 7. Repeat the experiment using buffer solutions of different pH values.

**Figure 6**

**(a)** What happens to the starch during the experiment?

☐ **A** It is converted into amino acids.

☐ **B** It is converted into sugars.

☐ **C** It is converted into glycerol.

☐ **D** It is converted into fatty acids.

*[1 mark]*

**(b)** Explain why a set quantity of starch solution was used for each repeat in the experiment.

.............................................................................................................................

.............................................................................................................................
*[1 mark]*

**(c)** Describe how the student could have tested for the presence of starch in **Step 5**.

.............................................................................................................................

.............................................................................................................................

.............................................................................................................................

.............................................................................................................................

.............................................................................................................................
*[3 marks]*

Figure 7 shows a graph of the student's results.

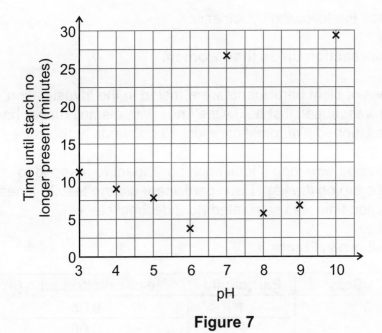

**Figure 7**

(d) Describe the trend shown in the graph in **Figure 7**, between **pH 3** and **pH 6**.

...................................................................................................................................................

...................................................................................................................................................

[1 mark]

(e) (i) The student thinks that one of the results shown on the graph is likely to be anomalous. Identify the anomalous result and give a reason for your answer.

...................................................................................................................................................

...................................................................................................................................................

...................................................................................................................................................

[2 marks]

(ii) Suggest **one** factor that could have caused this anomalous result.

...................................................................................................................................................

...................................................................................................................................................

...................................................................................................................................................

[1 mark]

[Total 9 marks]

**Turn over for the next question**

**Turn over ▶**

**6**  A scientist was investigating the reflex actions of men and women.

The scientist made the following hypothesis:

**'Men have faster reaction times than women.'**

The reaction times of eight participants were tested in the investigation.
Each participant was tapped just below the knee with a small rubber hammer.
When the leg was tapped it automatically kicked outwards at the knee.

The scientist recorded how long it took each participant to respond to
the stimulus of the tap on the leg.  Each participant did the test 20 times,
and a mean reaction time was calculated (to 2 decimal places).

The results are shown in **Figure 8**.

| Sex | Participant | Mean reaction time (s) |
|---|---|---|
| Female | 1 | 0.05 |
| | 2 | 0.06 |
| | 3 | 0.06 |
| | 4 | 0.04 |
| Male | 5 | 0.05 |
| | 6 | 0.04 |
| | 7 | 0.04 |
| | 8 | 0.05 |

**Figure 8**

(a) Using all the information above, give **two** reasons that support the idea that the
participants' response was a reflex.

.......................................................................................................................................

.......................................................................................................................................

.......................................................................................................................................

*[2 marks]*

(b) (i) What was the dependent variable in this experiment?

☐ **A**  number of participants

☐ **B**  stimulus

☐ **C**  reaction time

☐ **D**  sex

*[1 mark]*

**(ii)** What was the independent variable in this experiment?

☐ **A** number of participants

☐ **B** stimulus

☐ **C** reaction time

☐ **D** sex

*[1 mark]*

**(c)** **Figure 9** shows the mean reaction times for males and females in the investigation.

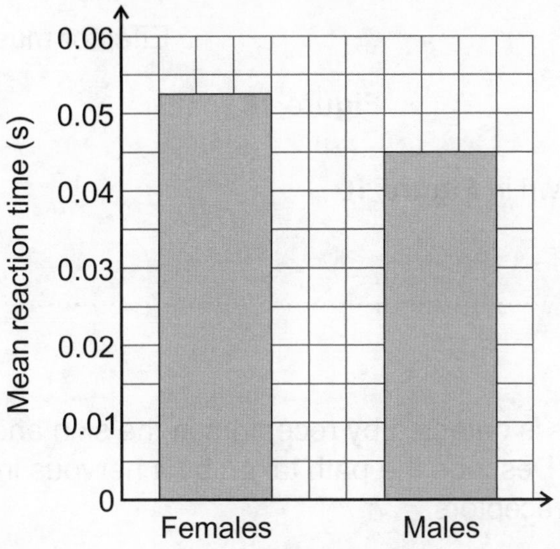

**Figure 9**

State whether or not the data shown in **Figure 9** supports the scientist's hypothesis. Explain your answer.

..............................................................................................................................

..............................................................................................................................

*[2 marks]*

**(d)** Suggest **two** variables that the scientist should have controlled in this experiment.

..............................................................................................................................

..............................................................................................................................

*[2 marks]*

**Question 9 continues on the next page**

**Turn over ▶**

Another example of a reflex is the response of moving your hand away from a painful stimulus. **Figure 10** shows the parts of the nervous system involved in this reflex.

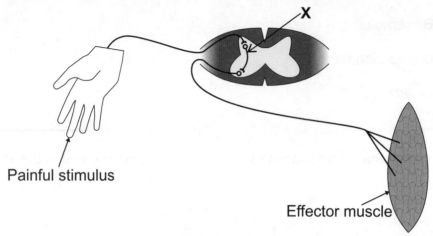

**X**

Painful stimulus

Effector muscle

**Figure 10**

**(e) (i)** Name part **X** shown in **Figure 10**.

.................................................................................................................................
[1 mark]

**\*(ii)** The pain stimulus is detected by receptors in the skin and causes a reflex response. Describe the path taken by a nervous impulse in this reflex, beginning at the receptors.

.................................................................................................................................

.................................................................................................................................

.................................................................................................................................

.................................................................................................................................

.................................................................................................................................

.................................................................................................................................

.................................................................................................................................

.................................................................................................................................

.................................................................................................................................

.................................................................................................................................
[6 marks]
[Total 15 marks]

**END OF QUESTIONS**

Practice Exam Paper
GCSE Combined Science

# GCSE Combined Science

## Biology Paper 2
### *Higher Tier*

In addition to this paper you should have:
- A ruler.
- A calculator.

| Centre name | | | |
|---|---|---|---|
| Centre number | | | |
| Candidate number | | | |

**Time allowed:**
- 1 hour 10 minutes

| Surname |
|---|
| Other names |
| Candidate signature |

**Instructions to candidates**
- Write your name and other details in the spaces provided above.
- Answer **all** questions in the spaces provided.
- Do all rough work on the paper.
- Cross out any work you do not want to be marked.
- You are allowed to use a calculator.

**Information for candidates**
- The marks available are given in brackets at the end of each question.
- There are 60 marks available for this paper.
- You should use good English and present your answers in a clear and organised way.
- For questions marked with an asterisk (*) ensure that your answers have a logical structure, with points that link together clearly, and include detailed, relevant information.

**Advice to candidates**
- In calculations show clearly how you worked out your answers.
- Read each question carefully before answering it.
- Check your answers if you have time.

**For examiner's use**

| Q | Attempt Nº | | | Q | Attempt Nº | | |
|---|---|---|---|---|---|---|---|
| | 1 | 2 | 3 | | 1 | 2 | 3 |
| 1 | | | | 4 | | | |
| 2 | | | | 5 | | | |
| 3 | | | | 6 | | | |
| Total | | | | | | | |

1   A student was investigating the distribution of buttercups in an area around his school.
    He counted the number of buttercups in 10 quadrats in five different fields.
    His quadrat measured 1 m². His results are shown in **Figure 1**.

| Field | Mean number of buttercups per quadrat |
|---|---|
| A | 10 |
| B | 35 |
| C | 21 |
| D | 37 |
| E | 21 |

**Figure 1**

(a)  What is the median of the data in **Figure 1**?

Median = ...................................................................

[1 mark]

(b)  The student used a random number generator to pick the coordinates to place
     the quadrats.
     Suggest why the quadrats were placed randomly.

     ..........................................................................................................................................

     ..........................................................................................................................................

[1 mark]

(c)  A week later, the student repeated his experiment in a sixth field, Field **F**.
     His results for each quadrat are shown below:

              6    15    9    14    20    5    3    11    10    7

     Using this data, calculate the mean number of buttercups per m² in Field **F**.

Mean = ......................................... buttercups per m²

[1 mark]

**(d)** Field **F** measures 90 m by 120 m.
Estimate the population of buttercups in Field **F**.

Estimated population = ........................................ buttercups

*[2 marks]*

**(e)** The student observed that the distribution of buttercups changed across Field **A**.
Buttercups grow well in damp soil, so the student thinks that the change
in the distribution of buttercups is due to variability in the moisture level
of the soil across the field.

The student wants to investigate the hypothesis that more buttercups
grow where there is a higher moisture level in the soil.
Describe how the student could investigate this hypothesis.

.................................................................................................................................

.................................................................................................................................

.................................................................................................................................

.................................................................................................................................

.................................................................................................................................

.................................................................................................................................

.................................................................................................................................

*[4 marks]*
*[Total 9 marks]*

**Turn over for the next question**

**Turn over ▶**

**2** Lactose is a reducing sugar commonly found in dairy products, such as milk and cheese. An enzyme called lactase breaks down lactose during digestion.
The resulting products are the sugars glucose and galactose.
These are absorbed into the blood from the small intestine.

**(a)** Suggest an explanation for why the breakdown of sugars like lactose into simpler sugars is necessary for organisms.

.......................................................................................................................................................

.......................................................................................................................................................

.......................................................................................................................................................

*[2 marks]*

**(b)** Glucose diffuses from the small intestine into the blood.
Describe how the concentration of glucose in the blood compares to that in the small intestine.

.......................................................................................................................................................

.......................................................................................................................................................

*[1 mark]*

**(c)** The optimum pH of lactase is pH 6.
State and explain what effect a pH of 12 would have on the break down of lactose by lactase.

.......................................................................................................................................................

.......................................................................................................................................................

*[2 marks]*

**(d)** Lactose intolerance is a digestive problem caused by insufficient production of lactase.
To test a person for lactose intolerance, they are given a drink of lactose solution.
A blood sample is then taken from them every 30 minutes for two hours.
The blood is tested to see how much glucose it contains.

Explain what will happen to the blood glucose level of a person who is lactose intolerant during the test.

.......................................................................................................................................................

.......................................................................................................................................................

.......................................................................................................................................................

.......................................................................................................................................................

*[2 marks]*

*[Total 7 marks]*

3   The lung is a specialised gas exchange organ.
    It contains millions of air sacs called alveoli.
    **Figure 2** shows an alveolus and a blood capillary.

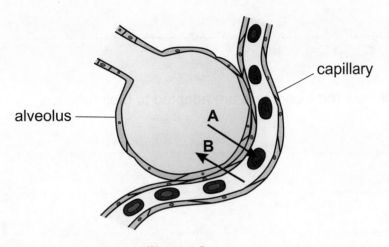

**Figure 2**

(a) The arrows in **Figure 2** show the net movement of two gases, **A** and **B**.
    What are the names of gases **A** and **B**?

| | | Gas A | Gas B |
|---|---|---|---|
| ☐ | A | oxygen | nitrogen |
| ☐ | B | carbon dioxide | oxygen |
| ☐ | C | oxygen | carbon dioxide |
| ☐ | D | carbon dioxide | nitrogen |

*[1 mark]*

(b) Explain why alveoli need a good blood supply.

..................................................................................................................................

..................................................................................................................................

..................................................................................................................................

*[2 marks]*

**Question 3 continues on the next page**

**Turn over ▶**

**(c) Figure 2** shows red blood cells travelling through a capillary.
Red blood cells are flexible, which allows them to fit through capillaries.

**(i)** State the function of red blood cells.

.................................................................................................................

*[1 mark]*

**(ii)** Explain how red blood cells are adapted to their function.

.................................................................................................................

.................................................................................................................

.................................................................................................................

.................................................................................................................

.................................................................................................................

*[3 marks]*

Sickle cell anaemia is a genetic disorder of the blood where the red blood cells become rigid and sickle-shaped. **Figure 3** shows a sickle-shaped red blood cell and some normal red blood cells.

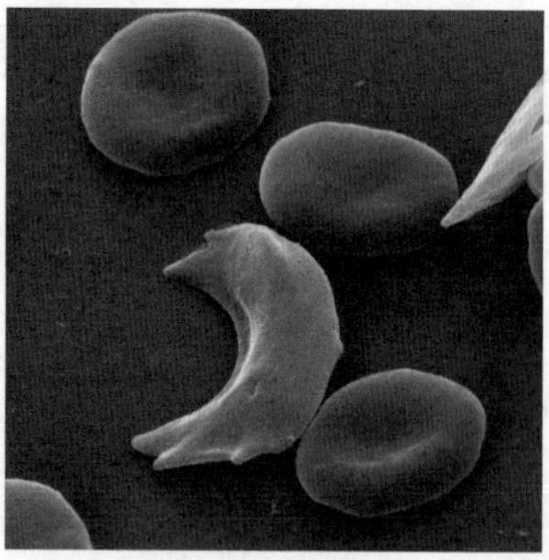

**Figure 3**

**(d)** A person with sickle cell anaemia may experience an increase in breathing rate. Suggest why they may experience this symptom.

.................................................................................................................

.................................................................................................................

.................................................................................................................

.................................................................................................................

*[2 marks]*

*[Total 9 marks]*

**4** **Figure 4** shows the carbon cycle.

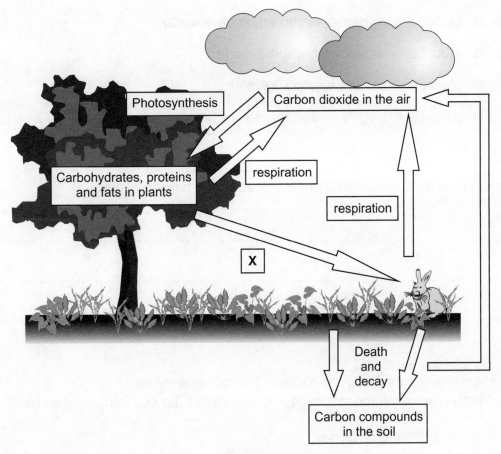

**Figure 4**

(a) Describe what is occurring at point **X** in the cycle shown in **Figure 4**.

.......................................................................................................................................

.......................................................................................................................................
[1 mark]

(b) Photosynthesis is an important process in the carbon cycle.

(i) Give **three** factors that limit the rate of photosynthesis.

1. ..............................................................................................................................

2. ..............................................................................................................................

3. ..............................................................................................................................
[3 marks]

(ii) Photosynthesis is an endothermic reaction. Explain what this means.

.......................................................................................................................................
[1 mark]

**Question 4 continues on the next page**

**Turn over ▶**

**(c)** What is the word equation for aerobic respiration?

- [ ] **A** glucose + oxygen → carbon dioxide + water
- [ ] **B** glucose → ethanol + carbon dioxide
- [ ] **C** glucose → carbon dioxide + water
- [ ] **D** glucose + oxygen → carbon dioxide

[1 mark]

**(d)** Explain how microorganisms are involved in the carbon cycle.

.........................................................................................................................................

.........................................................................................................................................

.........................................................................................................................................

[2 marks]

**(e) (i)** Microorganisms also play a role in the nitrogen cycle.
Which type of microorganisms turn nitrates in the soil into nitrogen gas?

- [ ] **A** nitrifying bacteria
- [ ] **B** denitrifying bacteria
- [ ] **C** nitrogen fixing bacteria
- [ ] **D** decomposers

[1 mark]

**(ii)** Some microorgansims live in root nodules on legume plant and turn atmospheric nitrogen into ammonia. Farmers sometimes include these plants in a crop rotation cycle to help return nitrogen compounds to the soil which are lost when crops are harvested instead of being left to decompose.

Give **one** other way that farmers can increase the amount of nitrates in the soil.

.........................................................................................................................................

[1 mark]

[Total 10 marks]

5   A scientist measured the rate of transpiration in two plants over 48 hours.
The results are shown in **Figure 5**.

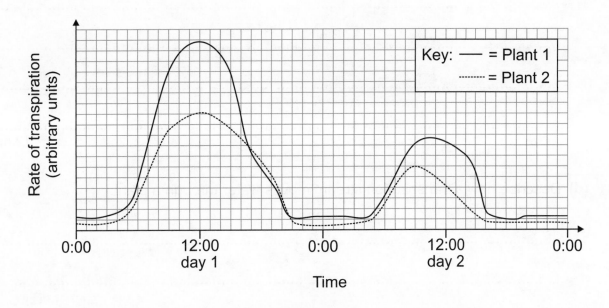

**Figure 5**

**(a)** Define the term 'transpiration'.

.................................................................................................................................

.................................................................................................................................
[1 mark]

**(b) (i)** At what time on **day 2** was the rate of transpiration highest for **plant 2**?

☐ **A**  06:00

☐ **B**  09:00

☐ **C**  11:00

☐ **D**  16:00

[1 mark]

**(ii)** The rate of transpiration for both plants was slower on **day 2** than on **day 1**.
Suggest **one** reason for this and explain your suggestion.

.................................................................................................................................

.................................................................................................................................

.................................................................................................................................
[2 marks]

**Question 5 continues on the next page**

**Turn over ▶**

**(c)** Explain why the rate of transpiration is lower during the night.

..............................................................................................................................

..............................................................................................................................

..............................................................................................................................

..............................................................................................................................

*[2 marks]*

**(d)** Describe how a transpiration stream moves water through a plant.

..............................................................................................................................

..............................................................................................................................

..............................................................................................................................

..............................................................................................................................

..............................................................................................................................

..............................................................................................................................

*[3 marks]*

**(e) (i)** Plants absorb water from the soil through their roots.
What is the process by which mineral ions are absorbed into the root?

☐ **A** diffusion

☐ **B** active transport

☐ **C** osmosis

☐ **D** transpiration

*[1 mark]*

**(ii)** Describe how roots are adapted for absorbing water.

..............................................................................................................................

..............................................................................................................................

..............................................................................................................................

*[2 marks]*

*[Total 12 marks]*

**6** In humans, sexual reproduction involves the reproductive system.

**(a)** The male reproductive system includes the testes.
What hormone is produced by the testes?

☐ **A** testosterone

☐ **B** adrenaline

☐ **C** oestrogen

☐ **D** insulin

*[1 mark]*

**Figure 6** shows the fluctuations in the levels of four different hormones during one 28 day menstrual cycle.

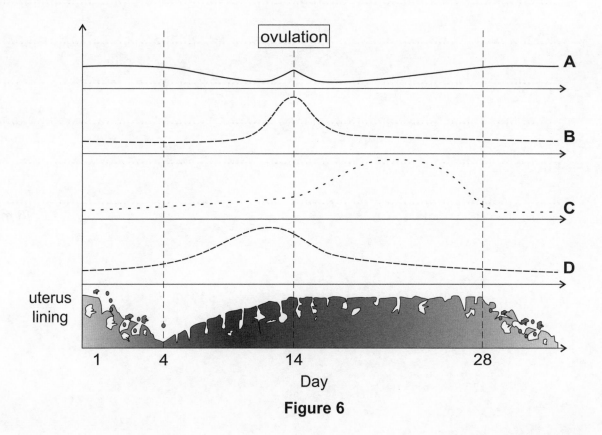

**Figure 6**

**(b)** State which line (**A-D**) in **Figure 6** represents progesterone and explain your answer.

..................................................................................................................................

..................................................................................................................................

..................................................................................................................................

*[2 marks]*

**Question 6 continues on the next page**

**Turn over ▶**

**\*(c)** Describe how progesterone, LH, FSH and oestrogen interact to control the menstrual cycle.

....................................................................................................................................

....................................................................................................................................

....................................................................................................................................

....................................................................................................................................

....................................................................................................................................

....................................................................................................................................

....................................................................................................................................

....................................................................................................................................

....................................................................................................................................

....................................................................................................................................

....................................................................................................................................

....................................................................................................................................

*[6 marks]*

Some methods of contraception use reproductive hormones to control fertility.
One such method is the contraceptive implant, shown in **Figure 7**.

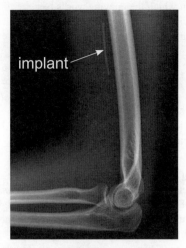

**Figure 7**

The contraceptive implant:

- is a small, plastic rod that is inserted by a doctor or nurse
- releases progesterone, which reduces fertility
- is effective for three years
- is over 99% effective at preventing pregnancy
- can cause side effects such as headaches and nausea
- can be made less effective by certain medications

**Figure 8** shows a condom. The condom is a barrier method of contraception.

**Figure 8**

The condom:

- is worn over the penis during intercourse
- prevents sperm from entering the vagina
- can only be used once
- is 98% effective at preventing pregnancy when used correctly
- protects against sexually transmitted infections (STIs)

**(d)** Use the information to evaluate the implant and condom as methods of contraception.
Give a conclusion of which you think is the better method of contraception.
Justify your conclusion.

.............................................................................................................................................

.............................................................................................................................................

.............................................................................................................................................

.............................................................................................................................................

.............................................................................................................................................

.............................................................................................................................................

.............................................................................................................................................

.............................................................................................................................................

*[4 marks]*

*[Total 13 marks]*

**END OF QUESTIONS**

# Topic 1 — Key Concepts in Biology

## Page 25
### Warm-Up Questions
1   mitochondria
2   Any two from: e.g. it has a long tail to help it swim. / It has lots of mitochondria to provide energy for swimming. / It has an acrosome to store the enzymes for digesting the egg cell membrane.
3   electron microscope.
4   $4.5 \times 10^{-4}$ µm

## Exam Questions
1   B *[1 mark]*

*Remember, DNA in prokaryotic cells floats freely in the cytoplasm — it's not stored in a nucleus.*

2 a)   C *[1 mark]*
  b)   It is the site of photosynthesis, which makes food for the plant *[1 mark]*.
  c)   They're involved in translation of genetic material in the synthesis of proteins *[1 mark]*.

3 a)   How to grade your answer:
  Level 0:   There is no relevant information. *[No marks]*
  Level 1:   There is a brief explanation of how to prepare a slide or how to use a light microscope. The points made are basic and not linked together. *[1 to 2 marks]*
  Level 2:   There is some explanation of how to prepare a slide and use a light microscope. Some of the points made are linked together. *[3 to 4 marks]*
  Level 3:   There is a clear and detailed explanation of how to prepare a slide and use a light microscope. The points made are well linked and the answer has a clear and logical structure. *[5 to 6 marks]*
  Here are some points your answer may include:
  To prepare a slide:
  Add a drop of water to the middle of a clean slide.
  Cut up an onion and separate it out into layers.
  Use tweezers to peel off some tissue from the bottom of one of the layers.
  Use tweezers to place the tissue into the water on the slide.
  Add a drop of stain.
  Place a cover slip on top by standing it upright on the slide, next to the water droplet, then carefully tilting and lowering it so it covers the onion tissue without trapping any air bubbles.
  To use a light microscope:
  Clip the slide onto the stage.
  Select the lowest-powered objective lens.
  Use the coarse adjustment knob to move the stage up to just below the objective lens (without looking down the eyepiece).
  Look down the eyepiece and use the coarse adjustment knob to move the stage downwards until the image is roughly in focus.
  Adjust the focus with the fine adjustment knob, until a clear image of the cells is visible.
  To see the cells with greater magnification, swap to a higher-powered objective lens and refocus.
  b)   real size = image size ÷ magnification
       = 7.5 mm ÷ 100
       = 0.075 mm
       $0.075 \times 1000 =$ **75 µm** *[3 marks for correct answer, otherwise 1 mark for correctly rearranging the equation and 1 mark for 0.075 mm.]*

## Page 31
### Warm-Up Questions
1   The part of an enzyme which joins to a substrate.
2   The pH at which the enzyme works best.
3   temperature and substrate concentration
4 a)   carbohydrase/amylase
  b)   protease
  c)   lipase
*Carbohydrases (e.g. amylase) break down carbohydrates, such as starch. Proteases break down proteins, and lipases break down lipids (fats).*
5 a)   (simple) sugars
  b)   amino acids
6   amino acids

## Exam Questions
1 a)   Accept answers between 38 °C and 40 °C *[1 mark]*.
  b)   Enzyme B, e.g. because it has an unusually high optimum temperature which it would need to work in the hot vent *[1 mark]*.
2 a)   To prevent the starch coming into contact with amylase in the syringe, which would have started the reaction before he had started the stop clock *[1 mark]*.
  b)   Rate = $1000 \div 60 =$ **17 s$^{-1}$** (2 s.f.) *[1 mark]*
  c)   Repeat the experiment using buffers with a range of different pH values and compare the results *[1 mark]*.

## Page 35
### Warm-Up Questions
1   Osmosis and active transport.
2   E.g diffusion is passive whereas active transport requires energy. Diffusion is movement from an area of higher concentration to an area of lower concentration, whereas active transport is from an area of lower concentration to higher concentration.
3   A partially permeable membrane only allows small molecules (e.g. water) to diffuse through it.
4   Osmosis is the net movement of water molecules across a partially permeable membrane from a region of higher water concentration to a region of lower water concentration.

## Exam Questions
1 a)   The ink will diffuse / spread out through the water *[1 mark]*. This is because the ink particles will move from where there is a higher concentration of them (the drop of ink) to where there is a lower concentration of them (the surrounding water) *[1 mark]*.
2 a)   The potato cylinder in tube D *[1 mark]*, because this tube contains the most concentrated sugar solution so this cylinder will have lost the most water *[1 mark]* by osmosis *[1 mark]*.
  b)   Tube A contained distilled water, so some of the water moved by osmosis into the potato cylinder *[1 mark]* from an area of high water concentration to an area of low water concentration *[1 mark]*.

# Topic 2 — Cells and Control

## Page 43
### Warm-Up Questions
1   It's the process by which a cell changes to become specialised for its job.
2   True

**3**    25% of two-month-olds are lighter than the baby.

**4**    in the nucleus

## Exam Questions

**1 a)**    The amount of DNA is doubling *[1 mark]* so that there is one copy for each new cell *[1 mark]*.

**b)**    The two new cells separate *[1 mark]*.

**c)**    two *[1 mark]*

**d)**    A change in one of the genes controlling cell division can cause cells to divide uncontrollably *[1 mark]*. This can lead to a mass of cells called a tumour, which can invade and destroy surrounding cells *[1 mark]*.

**2 a)**    E.g. they could be grown into a particular type of cell, which can then be used to replace faulty cells *[1 mark]*.

**b)**    Embryonic stem cells have the potential to develop into any kind of cell, whereas adult stem cells can only develop into certain types of cell *[1 mark]*.

**3**    3 hours = 60 × 3 = 180 minutes
180 ÷ 30 = 6 divisions
$2^6 = 2 \times 2 \times 2 \times 2 \times 2 \times 2 =$ **64 cells** *[2 marks for correct answer, otherwise 1 mark for correct working.]*

## Page 47
## Warm-Up Questions

**1**    A stimulus is a change in the environment.

**2**    An axon carries nerve impulses away from the cell body.

**3**    A myelin sheath surrounds an axon, acting as an electrical insulator.

**4**    sensory neurone, relay neurone, motor neurone

**5**    synapse

## Exam Questions

**1 a)**    Stimulus: appearance of red triangle *[1 mark]*
Receptors: cells in the eye / light receptor cells *[1 mark]*
Effectors: muscles (in hand controlling mouse) *[1 mark]*

**b)**    343 × 3 = 1029
1029 − 328 − 346 = **355 ms** *[2 marks for the correct answer, otherwise 1 mark for correct working.]*

**2 a)**    motor neurone *[1 mark]*

**b)**    Muscle *[1 mark]*, which contracts to move the baby's fingers *[1 mark]*.

**c)**    When the electrical impulse reaches the end of the neurone, it stimulates the release of a neurotransmitter *[1 mark]*. The neurotransmitter diffuses across the synapse to activate an electrical impulse in the next neurone *[1 mark]*.

**d)**    E.g. in a baby older than 6 months, the pathway will involve conscious parts of the brain, whereas in a newborn baby it won't. / In a baby older than 6 months, the response will not be produced as rapidly as in the newborn baby *[1 mark]*.

*The response in the baby older than 6 months is not a reflex — it chooses whether it wants to grasp an object. Remember, reflexes are automatic — they don't involve conscious parts of the brain, which makes the response much faster.*

## Topic 3 — Genetics

## Page 52
## Warm-Up Questions

**1**    two

**2**    A and T. C and G.

**3**    A section of DNA on a chromosome that codes for a particular protein.

## Exam Questions

**1 a)**    (ice cold) alcohol *[1 mark]*

**b)**    DNA *[1 mark]*

**2 a)**    C *[1 mark]*

**b)**    hydrogen bonds *[1 mark]*

**c)**    DNA contains genes *[1 mark]*. Each gene codes for a particular sequence of amino acids *[1 mark]*, which are put together to make a specific protein *[1 mark]*.

**3 a)**    three *[1 mark]*

*When a cell undergoes meiosis, each new cell ends up with half the number of chromosomes as in the original cell.*

**b)**    four *[1 mark]*

*Remember, when a cell undergoes meiosis, four gametes are produced — it doesn't matter whether you're talking about human cells or mosquito cells.*

## Page 57
## Warm-Up Questions

**1**    Different versions of the same gene.

**2**    What characteristics you have.

**3**    White fur, because you need two copies of the recessive allele (b) for this characteristic to be shown / if you have one recessive allele and one dominant allele (Bb) you get brown fur, so brown fur must be the dominant characteristic.

**4**    XX

## Exam Questions

**1 a)**

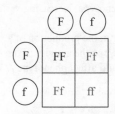

*[1 mark for correct genotype of offspring, 1 mark for correct genotypes of gametes]*

**b)**    1 in 2 / 50% *[1 mark]*

**c)**    Has cystic fibrosis *[1 mark]*.

**2 a)**    AA, Aa *[1 mark]*

**b)**    E.g.

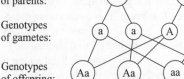

*[1 mark for parent with genotype aa, 1 mark for parent with genotype Aa, 1 mark for correct genotypes of offspring]*

**c)**    50% *[1 mark]*

*Offspring with the genotype aa will have albinism.*

**d)**    Fertilisation is random/the genetic diagram only shows the probability of the outcome, so the numbers of offspring produced will not always be exactly in those proportions *[1 mark]*.

## Page 61
## Warm-Up Questions

**1**    Differences between members of the same species that have been caused by the environment/conditions an organism lives in.

2 a) E.g. Amy and Beth could have inherited different alleles/ genes for hair type (curly or straight) from their parents.

b) E.g. one of the sisters might use curling tongs or hair straighteners to alter their natural hair type. / Amy might use curling tongs to make her hair curly. / Beth might use hair straighteners to make her hair straight.

3 False

## Exam Questions

1 a) D

b) The difference in weight must be caused by the environment *[1 mark]*, because the twins have exactly the same genes *[1 mark]*.

*In this case, the environment can mean the amount of food each twin eats or the amount of exercise they each do.*

c) No, because if it was caused by genes, both twins should have the birthmark *[1 mark]*.

2 a) E.g. if Eshan has the allele he could get tailored advice on lifestyle factors to reduce the likelihood of developing colorectal cancer. / He can have regular checks to ensure early treatment if he develops colorectal cancer *[1 mark]*.

b) E.g. if Eshan has the allele he could be discriminated against by life insurers / he could be discriminated against by employers / he could be put under pressure not to have children so that the gene is not passed on / he could have increased stress levels from worrying about potentially developing colorectal cancer *[1 mark]*.

3 a) Mutations change the base sequence of DNA *[1 mark]*, which can result in a new allele *[1 mark]*. New alleles can lead to differences in phenotype, increasing variation *[1 mark]*.

b) E.g the mutation could result in the production of a protein that is very different *[1 mark]*, so the activity of the protein would be affected, which would affect phenotype *[1 mark]*.

# Topic 4 — Natural Selection and Genetic Modification

## Pages 71-72
## Warm-Up Questions

1 Organisms with the beneficial characteristic are better adapted to their environment, so they have a better chance of survival. This makes them more likely to breed successfully and pass on the alleles for the beneficial characteristic to their offspring.

2 Any trace of an animal or plant that lived a long time ago.

3 E.g. genetic analysis showed that Archaea and Bacteria were less closely related than first thought.

4 Restriction enzymes and ligase enzymes.

## Exam Questions

1 a) New alleles arise though mutations *[1 mark]*.

b) i) Any two from: e.g. predation / competition for resources/food/water/mates / disease *[1 mark for each correct answer]*.

ii) They may lack the characteristics needed to adapt to the new selection pressure *[1 mark]* and so are less able to survive and reproduce *[1 mark]*.

2 a) The tall and dwarf wheat plants could be bred together *[1 mark]*. The best of the offspring/the offspring with the highest grain yield and highest bad weather resistance could then be bred together *[1 mark]*, and this process repeated over several generations *[1 mark]*.

b) There will be less genetic variation within the population of selectively bred wheat plants *[1 mark]*, so there is a smaller chance of disease resistance alleles being present *[1 mark]*. This means that there is a greater chance that all of the plants will be affected/killed by the disease *[1 mark]*.

3 a) Organism C *[1 mark]* because its DNA sequence has the highest percentage similarity to humans *[1 mark]*.

b) Archaea *[1 mark]*, Bacteria *[1 mark]*, and Eukarya *[1 mark]*.

4 Variation in the population meant that some *Clostridium difficile* bacteria had alleles which gave resistance to the antibiotic *[1 mark]*. When exposed to this antibiotic, resistant bacteria were more likely to survive *[1 mark]* and pass on the resistance allele to offspring *[1 mark]*. The resistance allele became more common in the population and soon all bacteria in the population were resistant *[1 mark]*.

5 How to grade your answer:

Level 0: There is no relevant information. *[No marks]*

Level 1: There is some information about evolution by natural selection. The points are basic and not linked together. *[1 to 2 marks]*

Level 2: There is some explanation about how evolution by natural selection may have led to a change in appearance of the stingray. Some of the points made are linked together. *[3 to 4 marks]*

Level 3: There is a clear and detailed explanation of how evolution by natural selection may have led to a change in the appearance of the stingray. The points made are well-linked and the answer has a clear and logical structure. *[5 to 6 marks]*

Here are some points your answer may include:
Ancestors of this stingray showed variation in their appearance.
The stingrays that looked more like flat rocks were better camouflaged and so less likely to be seen by prey, meaning they could obtain more food / they were less likely to be seen and eaten by predators.
This means they were more likely to survive and reproduce.
As a result, the alleles that caused the stingrays to look like flat rocks were more likely to be passed on to the next generation.
Over time, the flat rock appearance became more common in the population, until all of the stingrays in the population had this appearance.

# Topic 5 — Health, Disease and the Development of Medicines

## Page 77
## Warm-Up Questions

1 A state of complete physical, mental and social well-being and not merely the absence of disease of infirmity.

2 It can be spread between individuals.

3 Any two from: e.g. cholera / tuberculosis / some stomach ulcers / Chlamydia.

4 Sexual contact allows the exchange of infected bodily fluids such as semen and vaginal fluids. The exchange of such fluids transmits the virus between individuals.

5 E.g. wearing a condom when having sex. / Screening individuals so they can be treated. / Avoiding sexual contact.

## Exam Questions

1 a) An organism that can cause disease *[1 mark]*.

b) D *[1 mark]*

c) The fungus is carried through the air by the wind. / Diseased ash trees are moved between areas *[1 mark]*.

2 a) Malaria is spread by vectors *[1 mark]* and not through contaminated food/surfaces / skin to skin contact *[1 mark]*.

b) E.g. mosquitoes are the vectors of malaria, so destroying mosquitoes will prevent malaria being spread between people *[1 mark]*.

c) E.g. by having clean water supplies / hygienic living conditions *[1 mark]*.

## Page 82
## Warm-Up Questions

1 The skin acts as a barrier to pathogens, and, if it gets damaged, blood clots quickly seal cuts and keep microorganisms out.

2 To destroy specific pathogens that enter the body.

3 a (B-)lymphocyte

4 False

5 A placebo is a substance that looks like the real drug but doesn't do anything.

## Exam Questions

1 a) Mucus traps particles that could contain pathogens *[1 mark]*.

b) They waft the mucus up to the back of the throat where it can be swallowed *[1 mark]*.

c) hydrochloric acid *[1 mark]*

d) lysozyme *[1 mark]*

2 a) B *[1 mark]*

*Drugs are tested on human cells, live animals and human tissue in preclinical trials. If a drug makes it through the preclinical trials, it's then tested on human volunteers in a clinical trial.*

b) In a double blind trial neither the patient nor the doctor *[1 mark]* knows who is receiving the drug and who is receiving the placebo until all the results have been gathered *[1 mark]*.

c) E.g. dosage *[1 mark]*, efficacy/how well the drug works *[1 mark]*

## Page 88
## Warm-Up Questions

1 E.g. the National Health Service has to provide resources for the treatment of patients with non-communicable diseases all over the country. / People with non-communicable diseases may be unable to work, which may negatively affect the country's economy.

2 E.g. muscle weighs more than fat, so muscular people can have a high BMI even though they're not overweight.

3 E.g. they don't usually have any downsides/side effects.

## Exam Questions

1 a) E.g drinking too much alcohol *[1 mark]*.

b) E.g the cost of treating patients with liver disease in local hospitals *[1 mark]*.

2 a) A disease that cannot be spread between individuals *[1 mark]*.

b) E.g. nicotine in cigarette smoke increases heart rate which increases blood pressure *[1 mark]*. High blood pressure damages artery walls, which contributes to the build up of fatty deposits in the arteries *[1 mark]*. Smoking also increases the risk of blood clots forming in arteries *[1 mark]*. Fatty deposits and blood clots can both restrict blood flow, increasing the risk of heart attack or a stroke *[1 mark]*.

3 a) i) $\dfrac{\text{mass (kg)}}{(\text{height (m)})^2} = \dfrac{76.0}{1.58^2}$

$= 30.4 \text{ kg m}^2$ *[1 mark]*

ii) $\dfrac{\text{mass (kg)}}{(\text{height (m)})^2} = \dfrac{73.0}{1.58^2}$

$= 29.2 \text{ kg m}^2$ *[1 mark]*

b) Before : Moderately obese *[1 mark]*, After : Overweight *[1 mark]*.

# Topic 6 — Plant Structures and Their Functions

## Page 93
## Warm-Up Questions

1 False

2 A limiting factor is something that stops photosynthesis from happening any faster.

3 If the temperature's too high, the plant's enzymes will be denatured, so the rate of photosynthesis rapidly decreases.

*Remember, if the temperature is too high for an enzyme, the bonds holding it together may break. This causes the shape of the enzyme's active site to change, denaturing the enzyme.*

4 $\text{light intensity} \propto \dfrac{1}{\text{distance}^2}$

## Exam Questions

1 a) By counting the number of bubbles produced / by measuring the volume of gas produced, in a given time/at regular intervals *[1 mark]*.

b) Dependent variable — rate of photosynthesis/number of bubbles in a given time/volume of gas in a given time *[1 mark]*.
Independent variable — light intensity *[1 mark]*.

2 a) Light intensity *[1 mark]*, because between these two points increasing the light intensity increases the rate of photosynthesis *[1 mark]*.

b) After point B, increasing light intensity did not increase the rate of photosynthesis *[1 mark]*, so light intensity was no longer the limiting factor / a factor other than light intensity (e.g CO$_2$ concentration or temperature) was limiting the rate of photosynthesis *[1 mark]*.

3 $\text{light intensity} = \dfrac{1}{d^2}$

$= \dfrac{1}{7.5^2}$

$= 0.018 \text{ a.u. (2 s.f.)}$

*[2 marks for correct answer, otherwise 1 mark for correct working.]*

## Page 98
## Warm-Up Questions

1 The lower surface of leaves.

2 False

3 light intensity, temperature, air flow

## Exam Questions

1 a) xylem vessels *[1 mark]*

b) They are made of dead cells joined end to end *[1 mark]* with no end walls between them and a hole down the middle *[1 mark]*. They're strengthened with a material called lignin *[1 mark]*.

c) transpiration *[1 mark]*

2 a) phloem *[1 mark]*

b) Phloem vessels are made of columns of living cells *[1 mark]*, which provide the energy needed to move substances through the vessel *[1 mark]*. The cells have small pores in the end walls *[1 mark]* to allow substances to flow through *[1 mark]*.

3 a) $(10 + 11 + 9) \div 3 = $ **10%** *[2 marks for correct answer, otherwise 1 mark for correct working]*

b) How to grade your answer:

Level 0: There is no relevant information. *[No marks]*

Level 1: There is a brief explanation of how the increased air flow from the fan and the higher temperature increases the rate of transpiration. The points made are basic and not linked together. *[1 to 2 marks]*

Level 2: There is some explanation of how the increased air flow from the fan and the higher temperature increases the rate of transpiration. Some of the points made are basic and not linked together. *[3 to 4 marks]*

Level 3: There is a clear and detailed explanation of how the increased air flow from the fan and the higher temperature increases the rate of transpiration. The points made are well-linked and the answer has a clear and logical structure. *[5 to 6 marks]*

Here are some points your answer may include:

The movement of air from the fan moves water vapour away from plants in group D, maintaining a low concentration of water outside the leaf.

The low concentration of water outside the leaf increases the rate at which water diffuses out of the leaf.

Therefore, the plants in group D would lose more water, and so more mass, than the plants in group A.

At warmer temperatures, water particles have more energy to evaporate and diffuse out of the stomata.

The rate of transpiration will be higher in the plants at 25 °C than at 20 °C. So the plants in Group D will lose more water, and so more mass than the plants in Group A.

# Topic 7 — Animal Coordination, Control and Homeostasis

## Page 103
### Warm-Up Questions
1 target organ
2 a) E.g. pituitary gland, thyroid gland, adrenal gland, pancreas, testes.
  b) ovaries
3 adrenal glands
4 thyroid

### Exam Questions
1 a) a negative feedback system *[1 mark]*
  b) C *[1 mark]*
2 The pituitary gland releases a hormone/TSH which acts on the thyroid gland to make it release another hormone/ thyroxine *[1 mark]*. If this hormone/TSH is not released, then the thyroid gland will stop releasing its hormone/ thyroxine *[1 mark]*, so the person will experience symptoms linked to low thyroid hormone levels *[1 mark]*.

3 How to grade your answer:

Level 0: There is no relevant information. *[No marks]*

Level 1: There is a brief explanation of how the release of a hormone (adrenaline) in response to seeing the dog will affect the cat's heart rate and blood glucose level. The answer shows basic understanding, but lacks coherency. *[1 to 2 marks]*

Level 2: There is some explanation of how the release of a hormone (adrenaline) in response to seeing the dog will affect the cat's heart rate and blood glucose level. There is some attempt to explain why such a response is beneficial to the cat. The answer shows mostly accurate understanding and has some structure. *[3 to 4 marks]*

Level 3: There is a clear and detailed explanation of how the release of a hormone (adrenaline) in response to seeing the dog will affect the cat's heart rate and blood glucose level. There is a good explanation of why such a response is beneficial to the cat. The answer shows an accurate understanding of the relevant biology and is well structured. *[5 to 6 marks]*

Here are some points your answer may include:

When the cat sees the dog a nervous impulse is sent to the adrenal glands.

The adrenal glands release adrenaline.

Adrenaline travels to the heart, where it binds to specific receptor cells.

This causes the cat's heart muscle to contract more frequently, increasing the cat's heart rate.

Adrenaline also binds to receptors in the liver.

This causes the liver to break down its glycogen stores, releasing glucose.

This increases the blood glucose level.

The increased heart rate increases the rate of delivery of oxygen and glucose to muscle cells..

The increased blood glucose increases the rate of delivery of glucose to muscle cells.

Both these processes will help to increase respiration rate, to produce extra energy for a 'fight or flight' response / in case the cat needs to fight or run away.

## Page 108
### Warm-Up Questions
1 FSH/follicle-stimulating hormone
2 condoms
3 A fertility treatment that involves eggs being handled outside of the body.
4 Clomifene increases the release of FSH and LH.

### Exam Questions
1 a) It inhibits it *[1 mark]*.
  b) LH/luteinising hormone *[1 mark]*
  c) day 14 *[1 mark]*
  d) It breaks down *[1 mark]*.
  e) It will maintain the lining of the uterus *[1 mark]*.
2 a) Keeping oestrogen levels permanently high inhibits production of FSH *[1 mark]*, so no eggs will mature / so egg development and production will stop *[1 mark]*.
  b) E.g. progesterone stimulates the production of thick cervical mucus *[1 mark]*, which will prevent any sperm getting through and reaching the woman's egg *[1 mark]*. / Progesterone inhibits the release of FSH *[1 mark]*, which will stop a follicle/an egg maturing in the ovaries *[1 mark]*. / Progesterone inhibits the release of LH *[1 mark]*, which will prevent ovulation from occurring *[1 mark]*.

c) By preventing sperm from reaching the egg *[1 mark]*.

d) Advantage: e.g. they have no unpleasant side effects. / They protect against sexually transmitted infections *[1 mark]*. Disadvantage: e.g. barrier methods are less effective at preventing pregnancy. / They need to be available at the time of intercourse *[1 mark]*.

## Pages 112
## Warm-Up Questions

1 The maintenance of a constant internal environment in response to internal and external changes.

2 Removes glucose from the blood and makes the liver turn glucose into glycogen for storage.

3 A condition in which the pancreas doesn't produce enough insulin, or the body becomes resistant to insulin.

4 E.g. having a high body mass index/obesity.

## Exam Questions

1 a) D

b) Eating carbohydrates *[1 mark]*.

c) The pancreas/organ A produces little or no insulin *[1 mark]*. This means that the liver/organ B is unable to remove glucose from the blood for storage *[1 mark]*. So the blood glucose level is able to rise to a dangerously high level *[1 mark]*.

d) It makes the liver/organ B turn glycogen into glucose increasing blood sugar levels *[1 mark]*.

# Topic 8 — Exchange and Transport in Animals

## Page 119
## Warm-Up Questions

1 Any two from: e.g. metabolic processes/to build up larger molecules from smaller ones. / To contract muscles. / To keep body temperature steady.

2 E.g. carbon dioxide and urea.

3 Glucose and oxygen.

4 respirometer

## Exam Questions

1 a) C *[1 mark]*

b) The alveoli walls are thin *[1 mark]* which minimises the distance that gases have to move *[1 mark]*.

2 a) To release energy from the breakdown of organic compounds *[1 mark]*.

b) Any two from: e.g. aerobic respiration uses oxygen, anaerobic respiration does not. / Glucose is broken down fully during aerobic respiration but is only partially broken down during anaerobic respiration. / Aerobic respiration doesn't produce lactic acid/ethanol, anaerobic respiration does. / Aerobic respiration releases more energy than anaerobic respiration. *[2 marks]*

c) glucose *[1 mark]* $\rightarrow$ lactic acid *[1 mark]*

3 Surface area = $(2 \times 2 \times 2) + (2 \times 1 \times 4)$
$= 8 + 8 = 16 \ \mu m^2$
Volume = $2 \times 2 \times 1 = 4 \ \mu m^3$
So the surface area to volume ratio is **16 : 4**, or **4 : 1**.
*[3 marks for correct answer, otherwise 1 mark for correct surface area and 1 mark for correct volume.]*

## Page 125
## Warm-Up Questions

1 They carry blood back to the heart.

2 They help the blood to clot at a wound.

3 Any three from: e.g. red blood cells / white blood cells / platelets / glucose / amino acids / carbon dioxide / urea / hormones / proteins / antibodies / antitoxins.

4 cardiac output = heart rate × stroke volume

## Exam Questions

1 a) White blood cells *[1 mark]*. They defend the body against infection *[1 mark]*.

b) Any two from: e.g. they have permeable walls *[1 mark]*, so substances can diffuse in and out *[1 mark]*. / Their walls are usually only one cell thick *[1 mark]*, which increases the rate of diffusion by decreasing the distance over which it occurs *[1 mark]*. / They are very narrow *[1 mark]*, so they can squeeze into the gaps between cells *[1 mark]*.

2 a) A — aorta, B — vena cava, C — left atrium *[1 mark]*

b) It pumps blood around the body *[1 mark]*.

c) To prevent the backflow of blood *[1 mark]*.

d) Deoxygenated blood enters the right atrium *[1 mark]* through the vena cava *[1 mark]*. The blood moves through to the right ventricle *[1 mark]* which pumps it through the pulmonary artery to the lungs *[1 mark]*.

# Topic 9 — Ecosystems and Material Cycles

## Page 131
## Warm-Up Questions

1 a community

2 A community of living organisms (biotic) with the non-living (abiotic) conditions.

3 E.g. amount of water, light intensity, temperature, levels of pollutants.

## Exam Questions

1 a) E.g. they could have marked out a transect/straight line from the wood to the opposite side of the field *[1 mark]* and placed quadrats along it at regular intervals *[1 mark]*. They then could have counted the number of poppies in each quadrat *[1 mark]*.

b) E.g. the number of poppies increases with increasing distance from the wood *[1 mark]*.

2 a) At first, the population size of the cutthroat trout would decrease as the lake trout eat the cutthroat trout *[1 mark]*. This would lead to a decline in the population of the lake trout (as they'd have less to eat) *[1 mark]*. That would allow the population of cutthroat trout to increase again *[1 mark]*. The population of lake trout would then increase as they have more to eat (and the cycle would start again) *[1 mark]*.

b) E.g. competition with other fish species *[1 mark]*.

## Page 136
## Warm-Up Questions

1 Biodiversity is the variety of living organisms in an ecosystem.

2    Excess nitrates cause algae in the water to grow more quickly, which stops light reaching plants growing in the water. This means that the plants cannot photosynthesise, so they die and then decompose. This provides more food for microorganisms that feed on the decomposing plants. They increase in number, using up the oxygen in the water. This leads to the death of organisms in the water that need oxygen for aerobic respiration, like fish.

3    Conservation schemes maintain biodiversity by preventing species from dying out.

4    Any two from: e.g. food is added to the nets to feed the fish, which also produce lots of waste. The food and waste can leak into the water system, causing eutrophication and the death of wild species. / Open water fish farms can be a breeding ground for parasites, which can then escape and infect wild animals, killing them. / Predators can be attracted to the nets, become trapped in them and die. / Farmed fish can escape into the wild and can out-compete indigenous species.

## Exam Questions

1    E.g. black rats could compete with the island's indigenous species for resources *[1 mark]*. If the rats out-compete other species this could cause them to die out, reducing biodiversity *[1 mark]*. The black rats might bring new diseases to the island habitat *[1 mark]*. These new diseases might infect and kill lots of indigenous species, reducing the habitat's biodiversity *[1 mark]*.

*You don't have to have given these exact answers here. You get one mark each for giving any two sensible ways that introducing the rats could reduce biodiversity, and one mark each for explaining how each one could reduce biodiversity.*

2 a)   Planting only white spruce will result in low biodiversity because of the low number of tree species *[1 mark]*. A lower number of tree species will also mean that the number of different animal species using the trees for food and shelter will be lower *[1 mark]*.

   b)   E.g. protect the forest so that the natural habitat of the species is preserved. / Protect the species in a safe area outside of the forest. / Use a captive breeding programme to increase their numbers *[1 mark]*.

3    How to grade your answer:
Level 0: There is no relevant information. *[0 marks]*
Level 1: There is some information about the possible benefits of conservation schemes for species within the ecosystem, the people of Ecuador or people from other countries. The points made are basic and not linked together. *[1 to 2 marks]*
Level 2: There is some discussion of the possible benefits of conservation schemes for at least two of species within the ecosystem, the people of Ecuador or people from other countries. Some of the points made are linked together. *[3 to 4 marks]*
Level 3: There is a clear and detailed discussion of the possible benefits of conservation schemes for species within the ecosystem, the people of Ecuador and people from other countries. The points made are well-linked and the answer has a clear and logical structure. *[5 to 6 marks]*
Here are some points your answer may include:
If at-risk species go extinct it will affect all the organisms that feed on and are eaten by that species, so the whole food chain is affected.
This means that protecting at-risk species from extinction is likely to help maintain the biodiversity of the area, by ensuring minimal damage to food chains.

Protecting at-risk plant species may also protect the habitat of other animal and plant species in the ecosystem.
High biodiversity may bring more money to Ecuador through ecotourism, which will help to benefit the people of Ecuador. Ecotourism and the conservation schemes themselves will create new employment opportunities for local people.
Ecotourism also provides opportunities for people from outside Ecuador to see the rare species that live there.
Conservation schemes may help to protect species that are important to Ecuador's cultural heritage.
Conserving rainforest areas may protect plants that will, in future, turn out to be medically useful.
If these species were lost, people all over the world could miss out on valuable medicines.

## Page 142
### Warm-Up Questions

1    Fossil fuels release carbon dioxide as they are burned (to produce energy).

2    Salt water is boiled in a large enclosed vessel, so that the water evaporates. The steam rises to the top of the vessel, but the salts stay at the bottom. The steam travels down a pipe from the top of the vessel and cools and condenses back into pure water.

3    Nitrifying bacteria turn ammonia in decaying matter into nitrites and then into nitrates.

4    Using fertilisers increases the amount of nitrates in the soil. This increases the growth of the crops and so the crop yield.

## Exam Questions

1 a)   Animals are eating plants (and gaining nitrogen compounds from the plant proteins) *[1 mark]*.
   b)   denitrifying bacteria *[1 mark]*
   c)   nitrogen-fixing bacteria *[1 mark]*

2 a)   transpiration *[1 mark]*
   b)   Energy from the Sun evaporates water from the ocean *[1 mark]*, so the water molecule enters the atmosphere as water vapour *[1 mark]*. The warm water vapour rises, then cools and condenses into clouds *[1 mark]*. The water molecule then falls from the clouds as precipitation/rain/snow/hail into a garden pond *[1 mark]*.

3    How to grade your answer:
Level 0: There is no relevant information. *[No marks]*
Level 1: There is a brief description of one or two ways in which carbon stored in the vegetation could be returned to the atmosphere. The answer shows some basic understanding, but lacks coherency. The points made do not link together. *[1 to 2 marks]*
Level 2: There is some description of more than two of the ways that carbon stored in the vegetation could be returned to the atmosphere. The answer shows mostly accurate understanding and has some structure. *[3 to 4 marks]*
Level 3: There is a clear and detailed description of more than three of the ways that carbon stored in the vegetation could be returned to the atmosphere. The answer shows an accurate understanding of the relevant biology and is well structured. *[5 to 6 marks]*
Here are some points your answer may include:
Carbon stored in the small branches will be returned to the atmosphere as carbon dioxide when the branches are burnt.
The green plants could be broken down by microorganisms/decomposers, which will release carbon as carbon dioxide as they respire.

Some of the green plants may be eaten by other organisms. Some of the carbon from these plants will be released as carbon dioxide when the animals respire.
Some of the carbon from these plants will be lost as carbon compounds in the animals' waste. Microorganisms/decomposers will break this material down and release carbon dioxide as they respire.
Some of the carbon from these plants will be stored as carbon compounds in the animals' biomass.
This carbon will not be released until the animals are dead. It will be released as carbon dioxide by the microorganisms/decomposers that break down the dead material as they respire.
The wood that is taken away to be made into furniture will eventually return the carbon to the atmosphere through decay/burning when the lifespan of the furniture is over.

# Practice Paper 1
## Pages 149-162

1 a) Any two from: e.g. it has a nucleus / it contains mitochondria / it doesn't contain plasmids *[2 marks]*.

b) E.g. most cells have a structure that is specialised for their function, so they will contain different subcellular structures *[1 mark]*.

c) D *[1 mark]*

d) image size = real size × magnification
image size = 0.054 × 150
image size = **8.1 mm** *[2 marks for correct answer, otherwise 1 mark for correct working]*.

e) <u>Similarities</u>
Any two from: e.g. both plant and animal cells have a nucleus. / Both plant and animal cells contain cytoplasm. / Plant cells and animal cells both have a cell membrane. / Mitochondria are found in both plant cells and animal cells. / Both plant cells and animal cells have ribosomes *[2 marks]*.
<u>Differences</u>
Any two from: e.g. chloroplasts are present in plant cells, but not in animal cells. / Plant cells have a cell wall, but animal cells do not. / Plant cells contain a permanent vacuole, but animal cells do not *[2 marks]*.

2 a) Any two from: e.g. stop the mosquitoes from breeding / protect people from mosquito bites using mosquito nets / protect people from mosquito bites by using insect repellent *[2 marks]*.

b) B *[1 mark]*

c) 3 days = 3 × 24 = 72 hours
72 ÷ 18 = 4 divisions
1 bacterial cell × $2^4$ = 1 × 2 × 2 × 2 × 2 = **16 cells** *[2 marks for correct answer, otherwise 1 mark for correct working.]*

d) The body is injected with small amounts of dead or inactive pathogens (which are harmless) *[1 mark]*.
The pathogens carry antigens, which cause the B-lymphocytes in the body to produce antibodies *[1 mark]* and cause memory lymphocytes to be made *[1 mark]*.
If live pathogens of the same type are detected again, the memory lymphocytes can cause a much faster secondary immune response, so the person doesn't get ill *[1 mark]*.

3 a) B *[1 mark]*

b) E.g. research from the project about the cystic fibrosis gene could be used to develop more effective treatments for the disorder *[1 mark]*.

c) E.g.

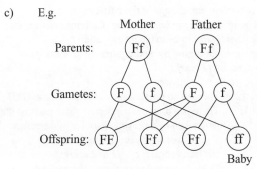

*[1 mark for showing that the parents both have the Ff genotype, 1 mark for showing the gametes' genotypes as F or f, 1 mark for correctly showing all possible genotypes of the couple's offspring and identifying the baby's genotype as ff.]*

d) Ff *[1 mark]*. E.g. Ian has the genotype Ff, so Leina must also have the genotype Ff in order for her children to inherit the genotypes: FF (Carys), ff (Beth) and Ff (Alfie) *[1 mark]*.

e) Environmental variation *[1 mark]*. The scar would have been caused by an environmental factor rather than being determined by genes *[1 mark]*.

4 a) Town B is the most polluted because it contains a higher percentage of dark moths *[1 mark]*.

b) 77% − 25% = **52%**
*[2 marks for correct answer, otherwise 1 mark for correctly reading 77% and 25% off the graph]*

c) Any one from: e.g. avoid leaving the moths inside the trap for too long. / Avoid touching the moths. / Release the moths in their original habitat *[1 mark]*.

d) The dark variety is better camouflaged in soot-polluted areas, so it is less likely to be eaten by predators *[1 mark]*. This means more dark moths survive to breed *[1 mark]* and pass the gene(s)/allele for this characteristic on to the next generation *[1 mark]*. As this process continues over time, the dark variety of moth becomes more common *[1 mark]*.

*It makes sense that if an organism blends in with its background it'll be harder for predators to spot it.*

5 a) B *[1 mark]*

b) To make the experiment a fair test. / To ensure the same amount of substrate was available in each experiment. / To make the results valid/repeatable *[1 mark]*.

c) They could have added the sample to a drop of iodine solution *[1 mark]*. If starch was present the iodine solution would have changed to blue-black *[1 mark]*. If starch was no longer present, the iodine solution would have remained browny-orange *[1 mark]*.

d) As the pH increases from pH 3 to pH 6, the time until the starch is no longer present decreases / the rate of reaction increases *[1 mark]*.

e) i) The result for pH 7 is anomalous *[1 mark]* because the time taken until starch is no longer present is much slower than expected *[1 mark]*.

ii) E.g. the student may not have used the correct volume/concentration of starch solution. / The student may have used the incorrect volume/concentration of amylase solution. / The student may have used a buffer solution with the wrong pH. / The student may have carried out the experiment at a different temperature. / The student may have started timing the experiment too early *[1 mark]*.

6 a) Any two from: e.g. there is very little variation in the mean reaction time among all participants. / Their reaction time was very fast. / Their response was automatic *[2 marks]*.

*If you have to think about what physical response to give then it's not a reflex action.*

b) i) C *[1 mark]*

ii) D *[1 mark]*

c) The men in this experiment had a faster mean reaction time than the women *[1 mark]*, so the data supports the scientist's hypothesis *[1 mark]*.

d) Any two from: e.g. the age of the participants. /
The strength of the tap on the knee. / Caffeine consumption
of the participants prior to the investigation /
Using the same timing method/equipment *[2 marks]*.

e) i) relay neurone *[1 mark]*

ii) How to grade your answer:

Level 0: There is no relevant information. *[No marks]*

Level 1: There is a brief description of some parts of the
path taken by a nervous impulse in the reflex.
The answer shows basic understanding,
but lacks coherency. *[1 to 2 marks]*

Level 2: There is some description of the path taken by
a nervous impulse in the reflex, but some detail
is missing. The answer shows mostly accurate
understanding and has some structure.
*[3 to 4 marks]*

Level 3: There is a clear and detailed description of the
path taken by a nervous impulse in the reflex.
The answer shows an accurate understanding
of the relevant biology and is well structured.
*[5 to 6 marks]*

Here are some points your answer may include:
The impulse travels from the receptors, along a sensory
neurone, to the central nervous system/spinal cord.
When the impulse reaches a synapse between the
sensory neurone and a relay neurone, it triggers
neurotransmitters to be released.
These neurotransmitters cause impulses to be sent along the
relay neurone.
When the impulse reaches a synapse between
the relay neurone and a motor neurone,
neurotransmitters are released again.
This causes impulses to be sent along the motor neurone.
The impulse then reaches the muscle/effector, which
contracts to move your hand away from the source of pain.

# Practice Paper 2
## Pages 163-175

1 a) Put data in order: 10, 21, 21, 35, 37
Median = 21 *[1 mark]*

b) To avoid bias. / To make sure the results were
representative of the whole sample area *[1 mark]*.

c) $(6 + 15 + 9 + 14 + 20 + 5 + 3 + 11 + 10 + 7) \div 10$
$= 100 \div 10$
**= 10 buttercups per m² *[1 mark]***

d) $90 \times 120 = 10\ 800\ m^2$
$10 \times 10\ 800 =$ **108 000 buttercups**
*[2 marks for correct answer, otherwise 1 mark for finding
the area of the field.]*

*Even if you got your answer to c) wrong, you still get full marks for d) if
you did the calculation correctly with your answer to c).*

e) Use a tape measure to mark out a line/transect across the
field *[1 mark]*. Place quadrats at regular intervals/next
to each other along the line/transect *[1 mark]*. Record
the number of buttercups in each quadrat *[1 mark]*.
Measure the moisture level of the soil at each sample
point and see how the number of buttercups changes
as the moisture level of the soil changes *[1 mark]*.

2 a) Organisms need to be able to break down sugars like lactose
into smaller components so that they can be absorbed
into the bloodstream and into cells *[1 mark]* to be used
for other life processes, such as respiration *[1 mark]*.

b) The concentration of glucose is higher in the
small intestine than in the blood *[1 mark]*.

c) Lactose would no longer be broken down *[1 mark]*
because lactase would be denatured *[1 mark]*.

d) Their blood glucose level will not rise very much at all
*[1 mark]*. This is because a person with lactose
intolerance has little or no lactase to break down
the lactose, so there will be little or no glucose to be absorbed
from the small intestine *[1 mark]*.

3 a) C *[1 mark]*

b) To maintain the concentration gradients of oxygen and
carbon dioxide *[1 mark]* to maximise the rate of diffusion
of the gases into and out of the alveoli *[1 mark]*.

c) i) To carry oxygen from lungs to the cells *[1 mark]*.

ii) Their biconcave disc shape gives them a large surface area
for absorbing oxygen *[1 mark]*. They don't have a nucleus,
so they have more room to carry oxygen *[1 mark]*.
They contain lots of haemoglobin, which combines with
oxygen in the lungs to become oxyhaemoglobin *[1 mark]*.

d) E.g. the sickle-shaped cells are more rigid than normal
red blood cells so they may not be able to carry as
much oxygen / the sickle-shaped cells are a different
shape from normal red blood cells, so they may not
be able to fit through the capillaries *[1 mark]*. This
could reduce the amount of oxygen transported to cells,
causing an increase in breathing rate *[1 mark]*.

*If you don't have enough oxygen for respiration, your breathing rate
increases to get more oxygen into your blood. In a person with
sickle cell anaemia, the lack of oxygen may cause their breathing rate
to increase so much that they feel breathless.*

4 a) Carbon compounds in the plants are being transferred
to animals as they eat the plants *[1 mark]*.

b) i) light intensity *[1 mark]*, carbon dioxide
concentration *[1 mark]*, temperature *[1 mark]*

ii) Energy is taken in during photosynthesis / the reaction
*[1 mark]*.

c) A *[1 mark]*

d) Microorganisms break down waste products and
dead organisms *[1 mark]* and release carbon dioxide
into the atmosphere as they respire *[1 mark]*.

e) i) B *[1 mark]*

ii) E.g. using fertilisers *[1 mark]*.

5 a) The loss of water from a plant's surface by
evaporation or diffusion *[1 mark]*.

b) i) B *[1 mark]*

ii) E.g. day 2 was less bright, so the stomata weren't fully open
and less water could move out of the leaves. /
Day 2 was colder, so the water evaporated/diffused
more slowly. / Day 2 was less windy, so the water
vapour was carried away more slowly, meaning
that diffusion couldn't happen as quickly.
*[1 mark for reason, 1 mark for explanation]*.

*The rate of transpiration varies throughout the day due to the changing
light intensity, but it can also be affected by the temperature, and the
air flow around the leaves.*

c) At night, the light intensity is low *[1 mark]* so the stomata
close, allowing less water vapour to escape *[1 mark]*.

d) Transpiration creates a slight shortage of water in the leaf
*[1 mark]*. More water is drawn up from the rest of the plant
through the xylem vessels to replace it *[1 mark]*. This in turn
means that more water is drawn up from the roots *[1 mark]*.

e) i) B *[1 mark]*

ii) Each branch of a root is covered in microscopic
root hair cells *[1 mark]* giving them a large
surface area for absorbing water *[1 mark]*.

6 a) A *[1 mark]*

b) C *[1 mark]* — e.g. because the level corresponds
to the thickness of the uterus lining, which is
maintained by progesterone *[1 mark]*.

*There are a few different ways that you can tell that this line
represents progesterone. As long as you're able to justify your answer,
you'll get the marks.*

c) How to grade your answer:
Level 0: There is no relevant information. *[No marks]*
Level 1: There is a basic description of how at least two of the hormones help to control the menstrual cycle, but little description of how they interact with each other. The points made are not linked together. *[1 to 2 marks]*
Level 2: There is a clear description of how at least three of the hormones help to control the menstrual cycle and some description of how they interact with each other. Some of the points are linked together. *[3 to 4 marks]*
Level 3: There is a detailed description of how each of the four hormones helps to control the menstrual cycle and how they interact with each other. The points made are well linked and the answer has a clear and logical structure. *[5 to 6 marks]*
Here are some points your answer may include:
FSH is released by the pituitary gland at the start of the menstrual cycle.
It causes a follicle in one of the ovaries to mature.
It also stimulates the production of oestrogen.
Oestrogen is released by the ovaries and causes the lining of the uterus to thicken and grow.
At a high level it stimulates a surge/rapid increase in levels of LH.
LH is released by the pituitary gland.
It stimulates ovulation and also stimulates the remains of the follicle to develop into a corpus luteum.
The corpus luteum secretes progesterone.
Progesterone maintains the lining of the uterus and inhibits the release of FSH and LH.
When the level of progesterone falls and there's a low oestrogen level, the uterus lining breaks down.
A low progesterone level allows FSH to increase so that the menstrual cycle can begin again.

d) Advantages of the implant: e.g. it works for three years / protection is always available / you do not have to remember to take a pill every day / it is highly effective.
Disadvantages of the implant: e.g. it has to be inserted by a doctor or nurse which may be painful/inconvenient / if certain medications are taken, a different contraceptive method would have to be used / you could suffer from side effects / it does not protect against STIs.
Advantages of the condom: e.g. it protects against STIs / there are no side effects / it is not affected by medication.
Disadvantages of the condom: e.g. it needs to be available at the time of intercourse / if it isn't used correctly it may not be effective / it can only be used once.
Conclusion: e.g. The condom is the better method of contraception because it prevents the spread of STIs.
*[3 marks for at least one advantage and one disadvantage of each method, otherwise 2 marks for at least two advantages or disadvantages of either method or 1 mark for one advantage or disadvantage of either method. 1 mark for giving a justified conclusion.]*

# Index

# Index

# Index